Praise for the film *What's On YOUR Plate?*

What's On YOUR Plate? is exactly the film we need now.

> —**MICHAEL POLLAN**, author of *In Defense of Food:
> An Eater's Manifesto* and *The Omnivore's Dilemma*

This film is charming beyond belief and covers a lot of great stuff. Thanks for making it.

> —**MARION NESTLE**, author of *Food Politics:
> How the Food Industry Influences Nutrition and Health*

Congratulations, Sadie and Safiyah! It is great to have you take us through the food cycle. As somebody said: "You are what you eat." Thank you for helping us get it right. You will definitely capture the imagination of your peers and generations beyond.

> —**KOFI ANNAN**, former Secretary General of
> the United Nations

We are, for the first time in our history, at the unenviable moment when our unhealthy diet and lack of education surrounding our food supply, has combined to foment the perfect storm that is taking us toward extinction. If we do not change what we feed our children and teach them about their food supply and the symbiotic relationship between a healthy planet, healthy food and healthy bodies—this path will become a reality. *What's On YOUR Plate?* will provide a first step in our education, which just might curb this trajectory and possibly save our children, their planet and all of our future.

> —**CHEF ANN COOPER**, author of *Lunch Lessons:
> Changing the Way We Feed Our Children*

It's amazing to see two young kids address the issue of where our food comes from in such a empowering way. We think everything .

> —**STEVE ELLS**, founder, chairman and co-CEO of Chipotle

What's On YOUR Plate? Well, what's on your ballot... So much of what we eat in America has to do with choices we make in the political realm. Unfortunately the under 18 constituency that is so affected by our food policy choices doesn't get to vote. I think this film will go far in focusing our attention on the way we're feeding the next generations.

> —**AARON WOOLF**, filmmaker of
> the critically acclaimed *King Corn*

I think that Michael Pollan's *Omnivore's Dilemma*, and his subsequent *In Defense of Food*, is to the food movement what Silent Spring was to the environmental movement. He did an excellent job of being eloquent about the industrial food system and how it ends up on our plate, and that's how I see this movie being for youth. It's an 11-year-old's take of *Omnivore's Dilemma* in a film for people to really be able to take it in bite sized pieces and understand it.

> – **DEBRA ESCHMEYER**, National Farm to School Network and the Center for Food
> & Justice

The girls sift through enough layers of the sustainable movement to make Michael Pollan proud: tackling everything from the origin of the food they eat, how it's cultivated and prepared, to the many miles it travels from its harvest to their plate to the tricky problem of what to do with leftovers.

> —**JULIE BLOOM**, *The New York Times* Urban Eye

[Sadie and Safiyah] have the most genuine sort of curiosity, and they astutely ask all the right questions.

Copyright © 2010 Catherine Gund
Foreword copyright © 2010 Kimberly Perry

All rights reserved.

ISBN: 978-0-615-40585-8

Library of Congress Cataloging-In-Publication
data has been applied for.

Published in the United States of America,
Printed in Canada

AUTHOR: Catherine Gund
PROJECT MANAGER: Mary Jeys
GRAPHIC DESIGN AND LAYOUT: Mary Jeys,
    Cassie Wagler, India Amos
EDITORIAL CONSULTANT: Tanya Selvaratnam
EDITORIAL ASSISTANT: Nate Buckley
RESEARCH ASSISTANTS: Angelica Modabber,
    Elona Jones, Bria Lewis, Geraldo Arias
PHOTOS: Catherine Gund, Lizbeth Angel,
    Marcia Taylor, Mrs. Q, Anna Lappé, Rachel Russell,
    Joel Blecha
COVER ART: Ellie Traggio and Tenzin Gund-Morrow
COVER DESIGN: Arlo Paust

DVD DISTRIBUTION: Bullfrog Films: John Hoskyns-
    Abrahall, Stephanie Miller, Sieglinde Fretz

ADVISORY COUNCIL: Kate Adamick, Dan Barber,
Chef Ann Cooper, Judith Helfand, John S. Johnson, Van
Jones, Jonathan Kevles, Anna Lappé, Katrina T. Monzón,
Raj Patel, Kim Perry, Michael Pollan, Dr. Robert Saken,
Anna Deavere Smith, Bryant Terry, Alice Waters, Aaron
Woolf

PARTNER ORGANIZATIONS: Slow Food USA,
Children's Aid Society, Alliance for a Healthier
Generation, Active Citizen Project, Garden Project,
James Beard Foundation, Lower East Side Girls Club,
Lunch Lessons, National Farm to School Network,
Nelson Institute, Solar One, Stone Barns Center for
Food and Agriculture, Cuyahoga Valley Countryside
Conservancy, Just Food, Manhattan Borough
President's Office, Small Planet Institute, NY Coalition
for Healthy School Food, Sustainable Table, Fair Food
Network, Sylvia Center

What's On YOUR Plate?

Catherine Gund

with Mary Jeys and Cassie Wagler

To my marvelous garden of children:
Sadie, Kofi, Rio, and Tenzin

And to my mother, Agnes Gund,
for planting the first seeds

Contents

FROM SADIE AND SAFIYAH

Safiyah and Sadie

Hi, Everybody!

This is Sadie and Safiyah. Welcome to Sadie's mom's book. We're in it a lot because we helped her make the movie called **What's On YOUR Plate?**. We've been best friends for a long time. We wanted to learn more about how to grow food organically, why lots of kids we know are having such a hard time with allergies and gaining weight and all kinds of medical problems, and why the cherry tomatoes from the farmers market in Ohio tasted so much better than the ones from our local supermarket in New York City. Sadie has high cholesterol that's genetic, so she had to eat much less of things she loves, like cheese. Sadie became a vegetarian partly to manage her high cholesterol. All of this makes us wonder if we are what we eat—and why.

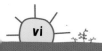

Safiyah's parents always taught her to think about what was in her food, but until we talked to farmers and people like Anna Lappé, we didn't know how hard the food companies try to hide what's really in the food. Kids are fooled into thinking that Snapple and Cocoa Puffs are good for them when they really aren't. When you think about what's inside the box and what it does to your health, those cartoons on your food packaging are not really so friendly.

We had so much fun making the movie. We got answers to a lot of our questions and met amazing people like the Angels, who are working hard to grow tasty, healthy food for the community on their family farm. We hope that the more we talk about food and why it's important, the healthier people will get. When people ask "Why go organic?", our answer is: "Who wants to eat chemicals?"

We started making the film at the end of fifth grade and finished it when we were in seventh grade. The experience of making the movie continued to influence our thinking when we did our final science project in eighth grade. We conducted an experiment where we tested the effect of different liquids on the growth of plants. Our test plant was a kidney

bean, and the liquids were tap water, East River water, V-8, ginger ale, and Muscle Milk. The East River water (very polluted) and Muscle Milk (very artificial) both killed the plants almost immediately; ginger ale killed the plants next; but tap water and V-8 kept the plants alive. If those fluids had that effect on the growth of plants, how do they affect our bodies?

You can try all kinds of experiments and projects like this in your home too. In our book, you'll find lots of activities you and your whole family can do to understand more about what's on your plate.

Thanks for reading. Let us know what you think by writing us at www.whatsonyourplateproject.org.

♡ Sadie
& Safiyah

FOREWORD

by Kimberly Perry

Global Campaign Director,
United Nations Foundation's Girl Up Campaign

Kimberly Perry

Each time I read an article reporting that one in three children are overweight or obese, I'm reminded of two things: one—we, as Americans, need a clearer lens through which to view nutrition and exercise. And, two—we need new voices to shed light on the issue.

What's On YOUR Plate?, through the lens of Sadie and Safiyah, sheds a curious light on the meaning of good food and good health. When these two young girls are empowered to ask a series of questions that build on each other, they find new meaning in the word health—the health of an individual and the health and sustainability of a community.

Eliminating the obesity epidemic in America is complex. It took us decades to get to this place. And no doubt, it will take us an equal amount of time to reverse the negative health impact of the past. This battle is a marathon, not a sprint. If we strive for balance and good healthy habits, we'll get there and sustain it.

Over the years, I've spoken with thousands of parents, educators, and caregivers who live in the dark of uncertainty and are daunted by the responsibility of keeping themselves and their children healthy. They aren't sure what to do, how often to do it—not even sure where to get started. I often suggest starting with perception. Start with the lens in which you view food and exercise. Do you see burden and angst, or convenience and energy? Self-indulgence or self-investment? When we begin to shift our perception of food and exercise to the light, the path of how to get there suddenly becomes a bit clearer. Through Sadie and Safiyah's journey, you will see the long-term health value, the fun, and the sense of community that good, healthy food and routine, physical activity brings.

The truth of the matter is that even as Americans begin to shift their perception and see healthy eating and physical activity as a cool, positive norm, we must ensure that policy leaders and decision makers transform our environment to make good choices easier to make, not harder. Those areas of environmental policy change must be in private industry (the innovators and manufacturers of what we eat and drink), our health care system (the providers who can guide us toward healthy living or who can treat us when we are ill due to preventable, nutrition-related illnesses), and our school system (where our children spend a good eight hours or more of their day). We must transform our legislative system to respect youth voice. Young people must be fully empowered to take charge of their health. If they are going to be healthier and reverse the statistics for the next generation, then they must lend their voices and lead the charge.

I believe **What's On YOUR Plate?** is a timely and important call to action. Sadie and Safiyah are an inspiration to the millions of kids across the country who have joined a movement to emphasize that the status quo isn't working.

In the early days of youth obesity prevention campaigns kids said, "I want to take charge of my health." And we thought that was it. But they came back and said "I want to learn how to be healthy. I want you to define that for me. I'm ready to take action." That's the importance of education. Young people are hungry for it. They are bombarded with so many mixed messages—so much marketing. They are ready to set the record straight.

Young people want to play an active role. I believe that adults can be great advocates, but until young people's voices are elevated—like Sadie and Safiyah—until they march to Capitol Hill, until they become the spokespersons on this issue, policies will remain the same.

We will achieve the necessary cultural shift in the way our country embraces nutrition and physical activity. I'm confident of that. Take this journey with Sadie and Safiyah and you'll see what's possible when young people step out front. The groundswell is strong. The movement is gaining momentum.

INTRODUCTION

Safiyah, Catherine, Sadie

"Eat your vegetables." I sound just like my mother when I say it, and I'm sure my four kids will sound like me one day. Home is the first place we learn about food, the place that shapes our relationships with food the most—at least until we get to a school dining room. I've worked toward having a healthy relationship with food in our kitchen, toward having my children understand the importance of where their food comes from, and toward eating ethically and responsibly. In our home, we spend a lot of time talking about food: why we like certain things, how we feel after we eat, why we choose to eat what we do, and what impact those choices have on our family, friends, and planet.

My daughter Sadie chose to become a vegetarian when she was nine. She'll gently and eagerly explain that she did

this because she didn't like how I cooked chicken… although I don't think my chicken is *all* that bad. I'm a documentary film-maker and one evening after a reasonable discussion about how vegetarians shouldn't just eat pizza and pasta (well, that was my side of the reasonable discussion), Sadie suggested that my next documentary film be about Vegetarians Gone Bad, starring her and her vegetarian friends, of which there are many, including her best friend Safiyah.

Furthermore, Sadie had recently been diagnosed with genetically high cholesterol. And, she was finishing fifth grade, about to start middle school. We live in New York City and Sadie was going to start walking by herself to and from school. She was going to eat lunch, and sometimes dinner and some-times breakfast, with a new group of people. I wanted her to internalize a sense of eating for her health and not just to satisfy a desire for instant gratification. And not just because I was there telling her what to do.

Sadie's vegetarianism, her high cholesterol, and her growing independence were three factors that created a perfect storm. I decided to take her up on the offer and make a film with her, but not one about bad vegetarians. Instead, **What's On YOUR Plate?** focuses on Sadie and her friend Safiyah's quest to understand the food they eat, where it comes from, and how it affects their bodies. Making the film together with the girls, I discovered that food is a powerful lens through which to see our society.

Take, for example, this chilling fact: these kids'

generation is the first in history to have a shorter life expec-tancy than their parents. Something is going terribly wrong. It's overwhelming to consider the grim realities facing my kids' generation. The Centers for Disease Control predicts that one in three of today's children will develop type 2 dia-betes. One in four fifth graders are obese. Already. They're only ten years old.

If this isn't the legacy we want, then what is the cure for the childhood obesity crisis? The crisis of packaged foods? The crisis of corporate greed? Our sedentary lifestyles? Our diets of sugar, fats, and salt? Agribusiness bulldozing out small farmers? Children preferring fast food to fresh, local, home-cooked food because fast food is all they've ever tasted?

The film **What's On YOUR Plate?** follows Sadie and Safiyah for a year while they explore their place in the food chain by farming, shopping, cooking, interviewing food providers and politicians, talking to friends and neighbors, and eating. When we decided to work together, I knew the kids could speak more clearly and more openly than adults. Without ever

being simple. Their curiosity drives the narrative. They
the film its urgency and its joy.

Over the course of making the film, I came to believe
that our kids *won't* have a shorter life expectancy if they are
empowered to ask a lot of questions. Why are we supposed
to eat three meals a day? How come apples are better for me
than apple juice? Why are companies making food that's not
good for us? How come we can't get fresh fruit in our school
lunch? Why aren't we growing vegetables in a school garden?
How come there are no farmers markets in my neighborhood?
Why is this chicken nugget in the shape of a dinosaur?

Sadie says, "We want people to ask questions. We want
kids to be more aware. And we want people to be healthy."
Safiyah continues, "We were really interested in this topic and
we got so curious. So when you're interested in something
you should just try to learn about it as much as you can, and
then go out and share your knowledge with the world." The
girls and I wanted to get people thinking. We found that you

can either tell people what to do, or you can share information
with them and let them make their own choices. We found
that the answers ultimately mattered less than the process of
questioning.

Sadie and Safiyah grew themselves a new community,
which includes their local family farmers and their elected
officials who are concerned about food fairness, the doctors
who care for them when they're sick and the chefs who teach
them to cook nutritious meals, the people who make their
school lunch and their classmates. We wanted to follow up
with some of our subjects from the film and to keep exploring
new stories. After the film was done, we kept asking questions.

We created an interactive website full of games, recipes, blogs, video clips, a store, links to other projects and
sites we love, a photo library, and more (www.whatsonyour
plateproject.org). We developed a curriculum for grades 4–8
to accompany the DVD that is now sold to schools nationwide.
Discovery's Planet Green broadcast the film so we wrote and
designed an online "Family Cook-In!" Toolkit. It is targeted
towards people of all ages to use when watching the film
at home. Every day we receive requests from people who
want to use the materials in their own communities to further
discussions on kids and food politics.

In response, lots of people started asking *us* questions,
which led us to keep asking others what they'd experienced.
We wanted to write this **What's On YOUR Plate?** book because
we learned so much from each other's questions, choices

and ways of seeing the world. It's our opportunity to take the **What's On YOUR Plate?** project a step further, to involve more children and families in the project and to keep connecting the dots. We identified seven kids to guide our exploration: Sadie, Caleb, Safiyah, Gabriel, Lizbeth, Ida, and Oliver. Each provided us with a focus. We asked them and their parents a lot of questions. We asked ourselves, "What can seven families, armed with little more than carrot sticks, do to help strengthen the food chain?"

We're caught up in a challenging, mostly impractical urban food web, but we have to start somewhere. Chapter 1 begins at home. Sadie gives you a glimpse into our kitchen, our meals, and why we eat what we eat. In downtown New York City, we have plenty of food options. There are lots of supermarkets, a growing number of farmers markets, tons of bodegas, and lots of restaurants—some that sell fast food and some that feature local, sustainable food. Not to mention the wide array of food carts and street vans selling prepared foods. Until recently, it was nearly impossible to escape the processed, high in fat and salt, fast food diet that rules this country, but through awareness and demand, the choices are increasing.

However, too many places are "food deserts" where reasonably priced, good food is more difficult, if not impossible, to find. Even in bustling cities like New York, food deserts are common, and predictably, located in the city's poorer neighborhoods. This makes it doubly hard for people on tight

budgets to purchase healthy, sustainably grown food. In Chapter 2, Caleb Wright tells us about his Harlem neighborhood, where some residents do not have enough access to safe and nutritious foods to meet basic dietary requirements for living an active, healthy life. Caleb's dad John had a heart attack at 42, which led the whole family to change their eating habits.

In Chapter 3, Safiyah takes us into her school's dining room to see an example of what more than 31 million kids are having for lunch every day. Where kids learn reading, writing and arithmetic, they also learn to eat. Safiyah and Sadie ask lots of questions; the answers lead to more questions. This process ultimately helps them see the complexity of the national school lunch effort, as well as ways to improve it. If kids are going to be on the healthy side of the national statistics, the school lunch program must be fully funded by the government; and every school must update its menu, training and food culture.

The statistics on food and health are daunting. One in four meals in the US is eaten at a fast food restaurant and

people spend 20 times more money at fast food restaurants than they did when I was a kid. *Twenty times.* Where it used to be once a month, some Americans now go every day. And now we know that even once a month was too much. Looking beyond the statistics, we see real people. Many of our friends became sick from what they ate when they were younger.

In Chapter 4, Gabriel Cubero-Albisa shows us what it's like to have food-related health issues including allergies, trouble processing sugar, and learning difficulties. He and his mother Cathy demonstrate how eating better can help in managing health challenges.

What will it take to reverse the growing trends of food related illness? One simple step is to meet and support farmers. As food writer and activist Michael Pollan has said, "Shake the hand the feeds you!" I believe that the people growing and raising our food need to be chosen and appreciated, like pediatricians. They need to be people we trust with our lives and the lives of our babies. They need to be people we know. My kids wear a T-shirt that says: "Don't buy food from strangers." One of the people who grows the food we eat is teenager, Lizbeth Angel. In Chapter 5, Lizbeth introduces us to her family and invites us to their farm so we can learn first-hand what it really takes to grow the vegetables we all need on our plates.

Since all families want their babies to have the best possible start in life, parents are deeply susceptible to advertising, medical advice, and the opinions of family and friends. It's

nearly impossible to make sense of the constantly shifting trends in how to feed and nurture babies. When I had my first baby, my community advised me to: "Seek out information, be patient and thoughtful, and ask lots of questions." In Chapter 6, new mom Anna Lappé shares her approach to choosing her baby Ida's first foods and making mealtimes meaningful. It's a family tradition to be conscious about food so Ida has already enjoyed a wide variety of farm-fresh vegetables and fruits.

In order for us all to be able to "eat our veggies," we have to fight for the opportunity to do so. In Chapter 7, we meet Oliver in suburban California who joined the growing, international movement to improve people's access to healthy food when he was just twelve years old. He started by planting a vegetable garden and fruit orchard in his backyard. He speaks up about food fairness wherever he goes, in his science classroom, at the farmers market, and on his Facebook page.

He is one of the many kids in this book and beyond, who are making changes that make all of our lives better. They may

feel a little scared and humbled by the bigness of the problems in our world and how small their individual contributions may seem. But they know first-hand the benefits of local food: more energy-efficient production, more prosperous farmers, healthier communities, longer lasting and better tasting fruits and veggies. These kids know where their food comes from, and it isn't the supermarket or the factory. They know it comes from trees and the ground, from gardens and nearby farms.

None of the kids nor parents in this book has a universal solution, but we all do have genuine, varied and effective approaches. Our tree-shaded paths are decorated with muddy handprints and cardboard tiaras, with mini beet burgers and apple slices for snacks, with cucumbers and nasturtiums growing in bedroom window boxes. Our version of going green is about finding a balance, making it work, and having some fun along the way.

Sometimes I worry that when they're older, my kids might find me quaint: "She patched our jeans." "We had pet worms." "She used our paintings as wrapping paper." "We always sat around the table and ate dinner together." But my hope is that they'll look around and see fruit trees near everyone's home. People's household bins will be

labeled: plastic, glass, paper, compost, landfill. And landfill will be the smallest by far. I hope there will be farmers markets on every corner, and that kids will be cooking dinner with their parents. And everyone will eat their vegetables not only because they taste good but also because they know that vegetables are good for all of us.

Love, Cat

Chapter One

WHAT'S IN YOUR KITCHEN?

Cat, Sadie, Rio, Kofi, Tenzin

Since Sadie was my first child, her birth started my adult relationship with food. I wanted to keep her new body fresh and pure. I had read about the growth hormones in cow's milk that cause cows—and the people who drink their milk—to mature too early and too much. I wanted her to grow strong from vitamins and sunshine, not rBGH (recombinant bovine growth hormone). She started drinking milk when she turned one, and I only gave her milk from cows that had not been injected with growth hormones, like rBGH, which is used in 2/3 of US cattle. I learned that Europe, Japan, Canada, and Australia have, in fact, all banned the use of rBGH.

I ground her baby food from the fresh fruits and vegetables on my plate. I tried to buy organic. Organic milk comes from cows who are not given rBGH or other hormones

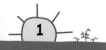

or antibiotics. Since the use of pesticides, herbicides, and insecticides on fruit and vegetable crops is so prevalent and dangerous, seeking out organically grown foods can make a difference. (See sidebar on Organic Farming on page 54.) Although "certified organic" doesn't go far enough in ensuring a sustainable food system, it does mean, for example, that many pesticides cannot be sprayed on the food, not *no* pesticides, just fewer. US growers use more than 1.2 billion pounds of pesticides a year, which comes down to about 5 pounds for each of us. I'd rather have fewer. I know buying organic food can be expensive, and it's hard to budget for families with growing kids, but I found that some fruits and veggies—like peaches, apples, strawberries, and lettuce—absorb more pesticides than others, so I prioritized buying the local, organically-grown versions of those.

Give-and-Take

I've influenced Sadie's eating habits, but so have many other factors, including her own tastes and needs. She has influenced my eating habits as well. It's a give and take that results in our ever-evolving combinations of energy-producing fare. When she was 8 years old, Sadie was diagnosed with severe, genetically linked, high cholesterol. She loves ice cream and cheese, but has learned how to control her cholesterol through diet. She balances her love of dairy with more vegetables and less fatty things like fried foods. Her desire to keep herself

What's the Dirt?

Most children can recognize over 1,700 products but do not know what's grown and produced locally.

healthy has sparked in her a curiosity and awareness about food, genetics, exercise, and disease. In fact, when Sadie and I started working on the **What's On YOUR Plate?** project, our discoveries affected the whole family.

Sadie and Her Brothers

Sadie and I and her three younger brothers, Kofi, Rio and Tenzin, live in New York, one of the fastest moving cities in the world, and it's hard to find the time to slow down and consider our habits, the current styles, and the heavy social pressures that reinforce them. Sadie and her brothers still laugh at me when I say no to processed snack food on our walk home from school. Almost daily, they hear me say: "How about an apple?", "I have water right here in my bag.". We shop at farmers markets when we can. And because we joined a CSA (Community Supported Agriculture), we try new foods and learn what's seasonal and what grows locally based on what the farm offers us. (See sidebar on CSA on page 12.) We make a point of only buying New York apples. But Tenzin loves avocados and Rio loves mangoes. Neither of those fruits is growing on any farm in New York, so we buy them at the supermarket rather than from a local farmer.

Sadie's brother Kofi regularly reads food labels telling us how much protein, fat, and sodium lurks inside. He offers comments on the nutritional value of foods he sees friends and family eating. Sometimes Sadie tells him to "stop being such an activist"—code for "annoying little brother." One night at dinner, Kofi performed a dramatic reading from the fair food author Michael Pollan's book *Food Rules*. When he got to rule #39, which says, "Eat all the junk food you want as long as you cook it yourself," Sadie interjected: "We already do that!" Which is true. We don't keep packages of cookies around the house, but we do make some from scratch every few weeks. Kofi's twin brother Rio inherited my dislike of chocolate, so half the batch has chocolate chips and the other half has walnuts. Baking desserts from scratch means no one feels like we're deprived of sweets, but we're spared the additives, preservatives and multiple chemical sweeteners of the store-bought brands.

When Sadie was a baby, we built window boxes for our apartment in an effort to make urban living healthier and more sustainable. We planted flowers and watched them grow. When she was four, she planted a few herbs—some basil, some mint, a rosemary plant—and they flourished. We used them in our cooking. It wasn't until her youngest brother Tenzin was born that we began experimenting with those tiny patches of land, growing strawberries, tomatoes, peppers, herbs, lettuce, beans, and squash. Eventually Tenzin became our family farmer. Toting around his orange water can, he's responsible for most of the planting, tending, weeding, and finally harvesting of our small yield of crops. Although last year's beans and strawberries failed, we're trying again this season with more varied breeds and a little more experience. We've added raspberries, cucumbers, eggplant, and three kinds of bite-sized tomatoes. We even planted Figgy the fig tree on our fire escape.

Luckily Sadie and her brothers like a lot of different vegetables. Or maybe I should phrase it differently, that luckily a lot of different vegetables have at least one champion in the family,

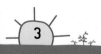

besides me. Some of the kids will eat string beans, broccoli, cucumbers, artichokes, and eggplant if lightly breaded and sautéed. Others like red, green, yellow, and orange peppers,

"cuz they taste like candy." They all love corn on the cob in the summer. Like many kids, they default to carrots. Like most kids, they can be picky. The only vegetable they all like is green beans and even then, one insists on having them raw, the other three, cooked. Nothing stays in great favor for very long; who knew you could "love, love, love" avocados one evening and "hate, hate, hate" them the next? In general though, the kids will finish off something green before the meal is over, especially if we're eating at home and they've helped cook.

Bad Food Is Never Cheap

There are so many good reasons for families to prepare meals at home rather than order takeout or eat a packaged meal heated in the microwave. It is often hard to pull off a nightly family dinner around the table, given how busy we all are, but it can be too easy to head to the nearest fast food window to pick up an instant meal. Knowing the story behind these foods helps us remember why it is better to stay home and make our own meals. As Sadie says: "Food that's bad for you is never cheap. It costs when you have to pay a doctor. It costs when you have to take medicine. And if you have to take medicine every day, you're paying again and again and again…" Unhealthy food is also paid for in part by our government through subsidies. As a result, the price we pay at the drive-thru window does not reflect the real price of producing that food. One of the reasons organic food is more expensive than conventional is that it's just not given the same breaks in the form of subsidies.

The problem with fast food starts with ingredients. Fast foods are high in fat, salt, sugar, and ingredients that end in "amate," or rhyme with "gross" (such as high fructose corn syrup (HFCS), maltodextrose, glucose). The federal government subsidizes corn more than any other crop, and a lot of corn is used to produce HFCS. It's in almost everything in the supermarket, from ketchup and bread to sweet drinks and even yogurt. The Corn Refiner's Association spends millions

Activity

Energy In ... ENERGY OUT!

1. On the next page write down what you did and ate yesterday. Underneath you can circle the symbol that best fits your food and activites.

2. Count up **all** your symbols and answer these questions.

FOODS

★ is for foods that you think are healthy and should be eaten everyday.

✓ is for foods you think should be eaten occassionally.

✗ is for foods you think should be avoided or eaten rarely.

ACTIVITIES

⇒ is for quiet activities -- like sitting in class, reading, playing the piano, or watching movies.

⇒⇒ is for medium activities -- like walking your dog, cleaning your room, or playing at recess.

⇒⇒⇒ is for vigorous exercise that gets your heart pumping and makes you sweat. It could be playing sports, riding your bike, chasing your friends, sledding, or even walking to school (if you walk fast and get your heart rate up.)

FOODS

How many ★ do you have? _____

How many ✓ do you have? _____

How many ✗ do you have? _____

What is your favorite ★ ? _____

Which ✗ could you do without? _____

ACTIVITIES

How many ⇒ do you have? _____

How many ⇒⇒ ? _____

How many ⇒⇒⇒ ? _____

Do you do a ⇒⇒⇒ everyday? _____

What other ⇒⇒⇒ activities would you like to try? _____

Energy In ...
ENERGY OUT!

Go through the story
and fill in the blanks → Yesterday for breakfast I ate _____ and _____ . It was
(food, noun)   (food, noun)
circle one ★ ✓ X   circle one ★ ✓ X

_____ . In the morning I _____ . Then I _____ and
(adjective)   (activity, verb)   (activity, verb)
circle one ⇨ ⇨⇨ ⇨⇨⇨   circle one ⇨ ⇨⇨ ⇨⇨⇨

_____ . For lunch I had _____ and _____ .
(activity, verb)   (food, noun)   (food, noun)
circle one ⇨ ⇨⇨ ⇨⇨⇨   circle one ★ ✓ X   circle one ★ ✓ X

To drink I had _____ . Then in the afternoon I _____ for awhile. I also
(beverage, noun)   (activity, verb)
circle one ★ ✓ X   circle one ⇨ ⇨⇨ ⇨⇨⇨

_____ and _____ . Tonight we ate dinner at _____ .
(activity, verb)   (activity, verb)   (location)
circle one ⇨ ⇨⇨ ⇨⇨⇨   circle one ⇨ ⇨⇨ ⇨⇨⇨

I ate: _____ , _____ and _____ . To drink I had
(food, noun)   (food, noun)   (food, noun)
circle one ★ ✓ X   circle one ★ ✓ X   circle one ★ ✓ X

_____ . And for dessert I had _____ . After dinner I _____ .
(beverage, noun)   (food, noun)   (activity, verb)
circle one ★ ✓ X   circle one ★ ✓ X   circle one ⇨ ⇨⇨ ⇨⇨⇨

_____ and _____ . The best thing I ate today was _____ .
(activity, verb)   (activity, verb)   (food, noun)
circle one ⇨ ⇨⇨ ⇨⇨⇨   circle one ⇨ ⇨⇨ ⇨⇨⇨   circle one ★ ✓ X

The best part of my day was _____ . My all-time favorite food is _____ .
(activity, verb)   (food, noun)
circle one ⇨ ⇨⇨ ⇨⇨⇨   circle one ★ ✓ X

My favorite sport is _____ . Tomorrow I am excited to _____ and _____ .
(activity, verb)   (activity, verb)   (activity, verb)
circle one ⇨ ⇨⇨ ⇨⇨⇨   circle one ⇨ ⇨⇨ ⇨⇨⇨   circle one ⇨ ⇨⇨ ⇨⇨⇨

And tomorrow I think I'd like to eat some _____ , _____ and _____ .
(food, noun)   (food, noun)   (food, noun)
circle one ★ ✓ X   circle one ★ ✓ X   circle one ★ ✓ X

of dollars on marketing campaigns that tell us HFCS is "natural," "contains no artificial ingredients," and is "fine in moderation." When we look more closely at HFCS, the scientific evidence tells a completely different story than the one they're pitching. For starters, The Food and Drug Administration has no formal definition of the term "natural," so their claim of "natural" is unregulated and hollow. HFCS is high in calories and low in nutritional value just like refined sugar. Consumption of HFCS and all refined sugar has been linked to obesity, heart disease and high blood pressure. Continuous use of HFCS can also cause liver disease, just like long-term, overuse of alcohol.

HFCS was first manufactured in 1957 by milling corn to produce cornstarch, then processing the starch to yield corn syrup (glucose). The corn syrup is then put through a chemical process by adding enzymes to it, changing it into fructose. It was substituted for sugar in soda and in all kinds of U.S. food products beginning in the late 1970's, when a tariff made importing sugar to the U.S. expensive and manufacturers needed to find cheaper ways of sweetening their products.

What's the Dirt?

Canned fruit can last on shelves for 100 years.

These days, HFCS is ubiquitous, showing up in unexpected places like ice cream and tomato soup. Aside from its use as a sweetener, HFCS is an inexpensive way of extending the shelf life of many processed foods.

Smart Choices?

Sadie wondered how much HFCS we had in our kitchen. One night, with Kofi's help, she combed through our cupboards and the refrigerator and scoured label after label for that ingredient. Although it is prevalent on the shelves of the supermarket, I had gotten most of our shopping list before this inquisition. But that night, we were able to talk about how misleading labels are across the board. The kids were confused by what's "healthy" and what isn't. Take cereal, for example. How do we figure out which cereals really deliver on their nutritional promises, like "now made with whole wheat" (Lucky Charms)? There have been arrows, stars, report cards and all kinds of healthy standards referred to on the fronts and backs of the boxes. For a time, a green check mark indicated that a product contained certain "nutritional benefits." Digging deeper, Sadie found that this Smart Choices Program™ was cooked up by the food industry itself. The campaign—which has since been discontinued for its glaring misrepresentations—anointed Froot Loops and Cocoa Krispies with the green check, despite how riddled they are with extra sugar and chemical compounds. Mayonnaise, Fudgsicles and Skippy's Peanut Butter also sported the green check.

This sort of deceptive packaging, marketing and advertising is everywhere. Both kids and adults are indoctrinated by television, labels, websites, and by the mainstream press to crave and buy certain foods. When you have purposely misleading packaging and advertising throughout the food culture, the pressure is on to find the right foods for your family. We are all up against at least a $1.6 billion ad budget of the food and drink industry, which supports 17,000 new food products each year. Those ads tend to be for processed foods… not crunchy snow peas and fresh lettuce. Have you ever seen an ad for purple cabbage, watermelon or kiwi fruit? If money has been spent to process and package it, then literally billions of dollars are being spent to advertise its existence and availability. It's shady. It's cynical. It's a big drag. But advertising is here to stay. Kids must be free to ask questions. Not just of advertising, but of food labels, government officials, peers, and even parents. We're all in this together.

My kids periodically succumb to the barrage of commercialized junk food and I'm not always there to monitor their consumption: they eat at friends' houses and with relatives who like to "treat" them to Oreos and Fritos. What they benefit from is good habits, knowing not to splurge on foods made with HFCS, and taste buds that crave a variety of natural foods. If they're lucky, they'll make truly smart choices.

Reading Between the Lines

Sadie and her brothers don't watch much television at home, despite the prevalence of playoffs at any given time in one sport or another. They're barraged with way too much advertising already. When Sadie was very little, she spent the night at her cousin's house. After she came home, I asked about what they did. She said they watched TV and had seen "The Cheerios Movie." I realized she thought an ad for Cheerios was a movie because she didn't know what commercials were. So I asked her how it was, and she said, "Short."

Many thousands of commercials later and Sadie has come to learn what advertising is trying to do. We regularly talk about magazine articles, movies, television, and advertising, about how stereotypes perpetuate assumptions, disrespect and cruelty. She sees how complicated things are. She is aware. One day Sadie noticed that some "wheat bread" is actually just white bread with molasses added to make it look brown and "healthier." She learned that the foamy milk in cereal ads—the bubbly, cool, refreshing looking milk that's being poured over the crispy, sweet flakes—was actually dish-washing soap. Things are not what they seem. Be ready.

A hard game, practice or any kind of workout, will make you hungry. It feels good to have a snack after all that running, jumping, sliding, gliding, shooting, and hitting. A healthy sports snack has a nice mix of carbohydrates and protein—and includes plenty of H_2O.

Sports Snacks

Not all sports snacks are created equal!
Take a look at how these two different snacks match up.

Factory-made Sports Snack

Natural Sports Snack

Energy Drink	(−) Lots of sugar! A 20 oz. bottle has as much as 7.5 teaspoons.
	(−) Contains High Fructose Corn Syrup.
	(−) 10 + ingredients include: food coloring, salt, preservatives and sunflower oil.
	(−) $100 million spent annually on advertising energy drinks!
Energy Bar	(−) More sugar! At least 5 teaspoons per bar.
	(−) Contains High Fructose Corn Syrup.
	(−) 20 + ingredients include: hydrogenated oils, soy protein isolates, and artificial flavors.
	(−) Billions of dollars spent annually on marketing.

Water	(+) Water is free!
	(+) No calories or sugar.
	(+) Your body is 70% water and loves hydration!
	(+) Flavor with mint, lemon or cucumber. Try different flavors on different days.
Trail Mix	(+) Make it with nuts, dried fruit, and seeds.
	(+) No preservatives or sugar added (check the dried fruit to make sure it doesn't have extra sugar or preservatives).
	(+) Contains protein, vitamins, and fiber.
Banana	(+) Good for repairing muscles.

Other good sports snacks: apples & peanut butter, carrots & hummus, cheese & crackers.

Marion Nestle's "Food Politics" blog (www.foodpolitics.com) is a great source of media savvy when it comes to food. It is the source of the Smart Choices Program™ takedown. She helps us read between the lines and conveys how tricky marketing and packaging can be. For example, internationally sugary cereals are made up of, on average, 40% sugar. In the US those same cereals are 55% sugar. Even when you read labels carefully to find low sugar and salt content cereals, you may still be vulnerable to subsequent changes. Cascadian Farms, an organic cereal company with humble beginnings, sold its Purely O's cereal to General Mills, who in turn decided the cereal needed more sugar, and perhaps a dash of high fructose corn syrup and tapioca—all without changing the label which had earned the trust of its customers. This change wasn't advertised—which means that loyal customers who have been buying the cereal for years may not be aware of the change, unless they know how to ask the questions.

Meal Times

My Mom wouldn't buy sugary cereals when I was a kid, and as a mom, I won't either. Unsweetened cereals are a breakfast staple of ours, along with long-cooking, unsweetened oatmeal. Sadie and the boys like to add maple syrup, walnuts, or raisins to it, and then they can easily monitor the sweetness. They also eat plenty of fresh fruit, grabbing bananas and apples from bowls on the counter or getting sliced pieces of crisp, cool cantaloupe from the refrigerator. I buy too many bananas on purpose since we eat them so regularly. They don't go bad, because when they start turning brown, Sadie peels them and puts them in the freezer to use later in smoothies or banana bread.

We keep yogurt, nuts, and whatever berries are in season, so that my kids can mix and match their own "parfaits" for breakfast, snack or dessert. We all like eggs, and we choose pasture-raised so we know the chickens weren't kept in small pens. Scrambled eggs are the first thing each of my kids learned to cook on their own. These days I'll often find one of them quietly stirring their eggs on the stove in the morning or after school. Two of the kids like them with cheese, and the other two don't. We don't drink store-bought orange juice since Rio loves to make fresh squeezed for special occasions. He even offers to strain out the pulp if we want. The kids make tea, both hot and iced, which is great for filling water bottles at sports games. We stay away from Gatorade or other sports drinks, which are full of sugar.

The kids don't eat school lunch. Instead, they pack home lunches, often with food from the night before. Using our dinner's salad, chicken, rice, or vegetables, they make sandwich wraps or a warm stew. We buy or make whole grain bread, and Kofi makes pesto, turkey, lettuce, and cheddar sandwiches. Sadie likes pesto with mozzarella and tomato. The kids also like to take raw veggies, such as sliced peppers, purple cabbage, green beans, and carrots. Hard-boiled eggs used to be a lunchtime favorite, but no one will take them anymore because their friends don't like the smell.

Everyone is free to peruse the cupboards and the fridge and put together snacks themselves. The kids especially like smoothies. They're so easy to make that even the youngest can do it himself by choosing any fresh or frozen fruit, throwing it in the blender, adding ice, milk and maybe some yogurt, a few nuts or seeds, oats and a dollop of honey. (See recipe for Sadie's Fruit Smoothie on page 13.)

While we're waiting for dinner, we often pull frozen edamame from the freezer, boil it, add a little salt, and have it as an appetizer. Sometimes we add corn and spinach (fresh when possible, frozen in the winter), which makes for a tasty side dish with the meal. Many families look to pasta as their dinner staple, but pasta is a side dish in our house, if we have it at all. It's usually plain whole-wheat pasta, sometimes with pesto or cheese on top. We love soups, although most canned and many boxed soups have tons of salt, so when I purchase

prepared soups and stocks, I look closely at the labels. One great shortcut is to have low-salt, organic vegetable or chicken broth on hand, if you can find it. Throw in your favorite vegetables and beans, and you have a quick, healthy, tasty soup.

We also try to keep on hand foods that will combine easily and make it simple to prepare a delicious, healthy meal. We always have plenty of rice, beans, vegetables, and cheese, which can be combined with tortillas, or eaten on their own. We add chicken, fish, or tofu, and usually eat it with a salad. (See Build-Your-Own Burrito recipe on page 75.) My kids love all the choices involved in making their own salads. I like to put out a variety of ingredients in different bowls: lettuce from our window garden, chopped raw veggies, fruits, nuts, oil and vinegar or different dressings. It's like having a salad bar at home.

In large part, what we eat—and what's in our fridge—depends on where we live, what foods, restaurants and markets are available. Where we shop, go to school, exercise, and play is determined by our physical community. In the following chapter, Sadie's friend Caleb will explore his neighborhood and explain how it has informed his family's habits and health.

What Is a CSA, Anyway?

A couple years before we started this project, our family joined a Community Supported Agriculture program, or CSA, to benefit from good food being grown around us. Here's how it works: in the spring, a farmer offers a certain number of shares to the public, often to a group of people in one neighborhood or town. Each member pays a fee before the season begins (it could be $330 for 22 weeks for example), and this covers the cost of one share of crop yields. Every week during the growing season, the farmer delivers freshly harvested produce to the designated pick-up area and members pick up their share. The farmer offers a different assortment of fruits and veggies every week including corn, peppers, cilantro, eggplant, kale, carrots, beets, squash, tomatoes, lettuce, and some surprises. Sometimes we get something we've never tasted before, but someone from our CSA always has a great recipe for trying it out.

If farmers provide for a CSA, as opposed to selling to restaurants, stores, or at farmers markets, they can focus on farming instead of marketing. They get paid for their work at the beginning of the season and regardless of the ups and downs of crop yields, weather, and pests. This shared approach to working the land helps keep small farmers in business.

To make CSAs affordable for most families, some may have sliding scale membership fees, accept food stamps, take payments over time, or subsidize low-income members. People are getting very creative in promoting CSAs. In Madison, WI, four health insurance providers offer a discounted premium if the applicant is a member of a CSA.

Today, CSAs are springing up all over the country—in Las Vegas, Detroit, Albuquerque, and Atlanta, as well as places already well known for their small, diverse farms. Tens of thousands of people are now members of CSAs, and in some parts of the country, there is more demand for CSAs than there are farms able to provide for them. The organization LocalHarvest.org has the most comprehensive directory of CSAs and farmers markets in the country: about 3,000 now exist, nation-wide. Check them out and sign up!

Salmon à la Julie

- ✓ 1 cup soy sauce (low sodium)
- ✓ ¼ cup orange juice or juice from ½ orange
- ✓ 1 tsp. ground cayenne pepper
- ✓ 1 tsp. ground ginger
- ✓ 1 Tbs. honey (optional)
- ✓ 1 lb. salmon fillet, cut into 4 strips
- ✓ 1 lemon, cut into thick slices
- ✓ fresh ginger slices (optional)
- ✓ fresh garlic slivers (optional)
- ✓ salt to taste (optional)
- ✓ black pepper to taste
- ✓ chopped or dried cilantro (optional)
- ✓ 4 parchment paper squares

Marinade may be used for dipping.

1. Preheat oven to 425°F.
2. In large bowl, mix soy sauce, orange juice, cayenne pepper, ground ginger, and honey.
3. Add salmon strips and let marinate while preparing parchment paper.
4. Cut parchment paper into 12-inch sheets. Fold in half.
5. Place salmon fillet on parchment, fold up on sides to create pocket.
6. Add marinade to each pocket.
7. Add ginger slices, garlic slivers, and lemon slices.
8. Sprinkle with cilantro, salt, and pepper to taste. (For extra flavor, add additional cayenne pepper.)
9. Fold parchment pockets in series of ½-inch folds until closed. Place on cookie sheet.
10. Cook 20–25 minutes, or until fish is cooked through, at 425°F.
11. After carefully opening pockets, place fillets on plates with lemon, garlic, and ginger garnish.

Sadie's Fruit Smoothie

- ✓ 2 bananas
- ✓ 1 cup plain yogurt
- ✓ 1 cup skim milk
- ✓ blueberries, raspberries, strawberries, mango, or any other fruit you like
- ✓ 1 handful of ice

Optional ingredients
- ✓ pinch of nutmeg/cinnamon
- ✓ handful of nuts, seeds/oats
- ✓ 1 tsp honey/maple syrup

When Sadie comes home from school, she makes a fruit smoothie for herself and her brothers.

1. Get your blender out.
2. Put the bananas, yogurt, and milk in the blender. (Use just one banana to make it frothier.) Blend until smooth.
3. Add fruit, ice, nutmeg, and cinnamon. Blend again until it's as smooth as you like it.
4. Pour a glass for yourself and one for a lucky family member or friend.

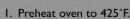

Beet Salad

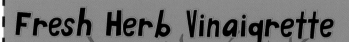

Recipe

- ✓ 4 medium beets, scrubbed, tops trimmed, root tails left intact
- ✓ coarse sea salt
- ✓ 4 Tbs. plus 4 tsps. extra-virgin olive oil
- ✓ 3 Tbs. red wine vinegar
- ✓ ½ tsp. Dijon mustard
- ✓ ½ tsp. agave nectar
- ✓ freshly ground white pepper
- ✓ 3 large bunches arugula, trimmed and roughly chopped (6–7 cups)
- ✓ 1½ cup candied walnuts

Inspired by a recipe from Vegan Soul Kitchen by Bryant Terry

1. Throw the beets in a medium pot, with 3 quarts of water and a teaspoon of salt, and boil them over high heat.
2. Once they are soft enough to pierce easily with a knife (20–30 minutes,) drain and peel (skins should slip off).
3. Preheat the oven to 400°F.
4. Cut tails off the beets, saving two tails for the vinaigrette (compost the rest!). Cut into ¼-inch dice.
5. Toss beets in a medium-sized bowl with 4 teaspoons olive oil. Transfer to a baking sheet lined with parchment.
6. Roast for 15 minutes. To cook evenly, rotate beets on baking sheet once. Take out of the oven and slide back into the bowl.
7. Add 2 tablespoons red wine vinegar, toss, and return the beets to the baking sheet. Cook the beets for another 5 minutes, take out of the oven to cool, and switch to vinaigrette mode.
8. Gather the reserved beet tails and the remaining red wine vinegar, plus mustard, agave nectar, ¼ teaspoon salt, and white pepper. Throw it all in a blender. Slowly pour in 4 tablespoons olive oil. If you feel like it needs more salt, now's a good time.
9. Get out your favorite serving bowl. Place the arugula pieces in the bowl first, then the roasted beets.
10. Enjoy the beets of your labor!

Fresh Herb Vinaigrette

Recipe

- ✓ ¼ cup vinegar (red or white wine is best)
- ✓ 1 Tbs. shallot, finely minced
- ✓ 1 clove garlic, finely minced
- ✓ ¾ cup olive oil
- ✓ ½ tsp. kosher salt
- ✓ Pepper (to taste, freshly ground tastes best if you have it)
- ✓ ⅓ cup minced fresh herb parsley, basil, oregano, chives or cilantro (or any herb in season now!)

Gina shared this recipe on our CSA blog. You'll see more from her here: http://tnscsa.wordpress.com

1. Whisk the liquid ingredients, shallot, and garlic.
2. Once it is smoothly blended, add the herbs, salt, and pepper.
3. Adjust as needed to suit your tastes.

Chapter Two

WHAT'S IN YOUR NEIGHBORHOOD?

John, Elijah, Caleb

Caleb Wright and Sadie became friends in elementary school. When he moved from the Lower East Side to Harlem, Caleb started going to a different middle school, but he and Sadie stayed in touch. Caleb lives with his father John and his little brother Elijah, whom he calls Jojo. Their new neighborhood has far fewer options for buying healthy food than some Manhattan neighborhoods, which until recently was not much of an issue for their family.

An Unwelcome Surprise

The Wright family had always been content to chow down on pizza, Taco Bell, take-out Chinese, and other fast food chains, which are sadly concentrated in low-income neighborhoods.

No one in the family was eating enough fruits and vegetables. Caleb's single dad, John, has a demanding job, so he doesn't have a lot of time to cook meals for his family, and good nutrition wasn't something he used to prioritize after a long day. Suddenly, in 2007, John suffered a severe heart attack and underwent emergency triple bypass surgery. He was 42 years old.

Over the twenty years before his heart attack, John had put on an average of five pounds a year; which meant that at the time of his heart attack, he was 100 pounds heavier than he'd been when he graduated college. Caleb and Jojo would join their dad in midnight snacks, usually cheeseburgers or egg sandwiches with bacon on white rolls with lots of salt. They ate out or ordered take-out almost every night of the week. Caleb's usual was sesame chicken or Lo Mein, sometimes both. They drank soda and other sugary drinks from the fridge at all times of the day. Moreover, even though their

routine involved a lot of running around, they weren't getting regular exercise. They often stayed up until 1 or 2 a.m. and nobody got enough sleep. John's stomach had gotten so big that Caleb and Jojo nicknamed it "Edward."

Although there is a history of heart disease in Caleb's family–Caleb's grandfather died of it–his dad's life-threatening heart attack in his early forties came as a shock. Caleb remembers, "I felt pretty weird because I knew that we weren't eating that well, but I didn't think it would lead to a heart attack. That made me think that we should get better food. I felt kind of sad because we didn't get to eat right when we could have and then he ended up getting his chest cut open." It was terrifying for the whole family.

At the urging of his doctor, Caleb's dad began to reevaluate everything about his family's diet. He realized that he was passing on bad eating habits to his kids. He says in the back of his mind he'd always known that what he was eating wasn't good for them, but he hadn't given a whole lot of thought to

What's the Dirt?

In 2001, Americans consumed 15 billion gallons of soft drinks, twice as much as in 1974 and equivalent to 587 12-ounce servings per year for every man, woman and child.

the relationship between food, health and the messages he was sending to his kids.

Food Insecurity

When Caleb's dad walked around their neighborhood, he saw primarily the kind of fast-food restaurants, take-out places and bodegas that had made it so convenient to eat poorly before. There were few supermarkets in the neighborhood and the ones that were there didn't stock much (if any) fresh produce, fish, or healthier meats. Organics were even harder to come by. Finding low-fat milk was a chore.

Too many places are "food deserts" like Harlem, where reasonably priced, healthy food is difficult, if not impossible, to find. Food deserts are predictably located in a city's poorer neighborhoods. This makes it doubly hard for people on tight budgets to purchase healthy, sustainably grown food. Residents then become "food insecure" which means they don't have access to safe and nutritious foods to meet basic dietary requirements for living an active, healthy life.

The picture of what "under-nourished" looks like is changing as we eat cheaper foods with more additives and fewer truly natural ingredients. For the first time in history, the number of people in the United States who are obese has surpassed the number who are underweight due to hunger. Because of the national scope of this crisis, we must take action to push for policy reform at the highest levels, which can be crafted to address systemic problems. We need to understand what's happening so we can best organize to pressure our elected officials and make national, regional and local improvements. At the same time, we must continue to make changes in our individual lives.

Caleb's dad knew that his family was living in a food desert. Although Harlem has changed dramatically since the real estate boom in the late 90's, it's still one of NYC's lowest income neighborhoods. About half of its residents are African American, who are almost twice as likely to get diabetes as non-Hispanic whites; nearly 15% of African Americans have diagnosed or undiagnosed diabetes. Most diabetics have high blood pressure and heart disease is the leading cause of death among diabetics. Access to healthy, nutritious food in Harlem should be a number one priority.

Getting Healthy Food into Our Neighborhoods

Many programs have been introduced to address the obesity issue in America, including those of the White House. In 2010, the First Lady Michelle Obama launched a campaign against childhood obesity, called Let's Move!. She also started a vegetable garden on the White House grounds to shine light on the many benefits of gardening at home. People all over the country—educators, medical professionals, parents, politicians, farmers, and chefs—are making inroads. With Sadie and Safiyah, Caleb discovered both new and longstanding programs in his own neighborhood that his family hadn't realized were right there.

Harvest Home Farmers Market in Harlem epitomizes what can be done by a passionate, determined person working to build a community. In 1993, Maritza Wellington Owens founded the organization to bring high-quality, locally grown produce to Harlem. Over the years, Maritza has sponsored farmers markets and provided nutritional and food preparation instruction for her neighbors, many of them low-income families. And all of Maritza's markets accept food stamps. We first met her through Manhattan Borough President Scott Stringer, who is an advocate of healthier food options and a valuable partner of **What's On YOUR Plate?**. Maritza invited Caleb and his family to the farmers market she runs a few blocks from their apartment.

There are now thirteen farmers markets under the

Harvest Home umbrella. Every season new ones are added, including one in 2010 on the grounds of a Bronx hospital where patients, employees and local residents can buy healthy produce without having to run around town looking for it.

On days the markets were closed, Caleb and other customers went to the corner stores and said, "How come you don't have any fresh fruits or vegetables? If you sold those things here, I'd buy them." As a result, a few began stocking Maritza's farm-fresh greens, squash and cucumbers. By demonstrating demand, people are inspiring better supply. In this way, change is seeping into the fabric of our city.

Caleb's Food Story

One small development in Caleb's neighborhood and all of a sudden dinner in their home has never been the same. At Maritza's market, Jojo loves the carrots and buys as many bunches as he can carry, and John has found a convenient source of organic greens. Since their kitchen is stocked completely differently, they eat at home most nights, experimenting

family stopped buying soda and installed a water cooler at home. Now they have a juicer so they can make their own fruit and vegetable juices including Caleb's favorite: a combo of celery, apple, lemon and fresh ginger. John has drastically reduced the family's salt and sugar intake in many other ways, like buying only sugar-free cereals for breakfast. Jojo now has oatmeal almost every morning, and his dad (like so many of us parents!) eats up the leftovers. Even the way they spend time together has changed. They shop together, and TV-time includes cooking shows to inspire variety in their home-cooked meals.

Walking the Walk

Cooking show or not, watching TV and sitting at the computer are part of sedentary lifestyles that will need to change if we're going to combat the obesity epidemic. After his father's surgery, Caleb saw John become more active. John started

with different ingredients. They've sampled a rainbow assortment of vegetables. Spinach is their favorite—steamed, with a little olive oil and garlic. Instead of factory-grown ham on processed white bread with mayonnaise for lunch, they put free-range turkey in a whole-wheat wrap with mustard. They eliminated red meat from their menu entirely, and his dad makes fish three times a week. When they eat out, they get sushi. When they buy chicken, it's skinless. They make substitutions for other old favorites, for example, cooking meatballs and meatloaf out of ground turkey, instead of beef. (See recipe for Caleb's Favorite Turkey Meatloaf on page 25.)

Fried foods, processed pasta and white rice are particularly hard for Caleb's dad to give up since they'd been a staple of the diet he'd grown up eating. The midnight snacks are much less common and feel like a special treat now. The

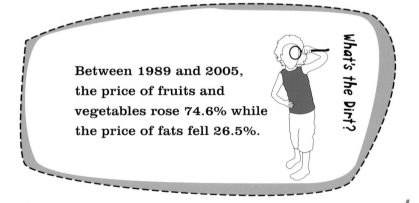

Between 1989 and 2005, the price of fruits and vegetables rose 74.6% while the price of fats fell 26.5%.

What's the Dirt?

going to the gym regularly and taking karate lessons. His example was inspiring. Caleb and Jojo enrolled in swimming and fencing classes and Caleb became Sadie's favorite jousting partner. Jojo began taking gymnastics classes and playing soccer. All three are more active than ever, regularly breaking a sweat.

Where we live dictates a lot about *how* we live. We not only have to ask if there's a farmers market within walking distance from our home, but also if there is public transportation like a bus system or rail line that goes from near your home to near your school or workplace. How far is your commute? Is there a playground, soccer field, basketball court, park, or public swimming pool in the vicinity? Are the streets safe for you to ride your bike? To walk on? Are there sidewalks?

Caleb takes the subway to school, and plays in the parks near there. Harlem has Central Park to its south which means there are trees, paths and fields where people can exercise and enjoy themselves. But the subway doesn't go to all parts of the city. In some areas, playgrounds are hard to find or have been left to decay which makes them dangerous to play in. Responding to this problem, Maritza Owens

and Harvest Home are collaborating with other public and private organizations to open a new playground called Play Street near Caleb's house. The goal is to give kids access to fun physical activities and programs, such as the arts, health and nutrition. Making excellent connections, this initiative is a perfect example of how communities can band together to make a positive impact.

Evaluating our Own Neighborhoods

How do we evaluate our own neighborhoods and the kinds of food they have to offer? If our main source of food is a supermarket chain of some kind, how do we effectively interact with the various store managers, to get to the bottom of such issues as whether the chicken carried in those stores is the highest quality possible, free-range, organic, antibiotic-free; whether the majority of the produce offered is locally and sustainably grown, and if not, why not; whether there can be a wider offering of wild fish, of sustainably produced dairy products, of foods that are packaged in a more environmentally conscious

WHERE DO YOU LIVE?

↓

CIRCLE THE ONES THAT DESCRIBE WHERE YOU LIVE:

I live: in the country in a small town in a big city in a medium-sized city on a farm

in a house in an apartment on a boat on a quiet street on a busy street

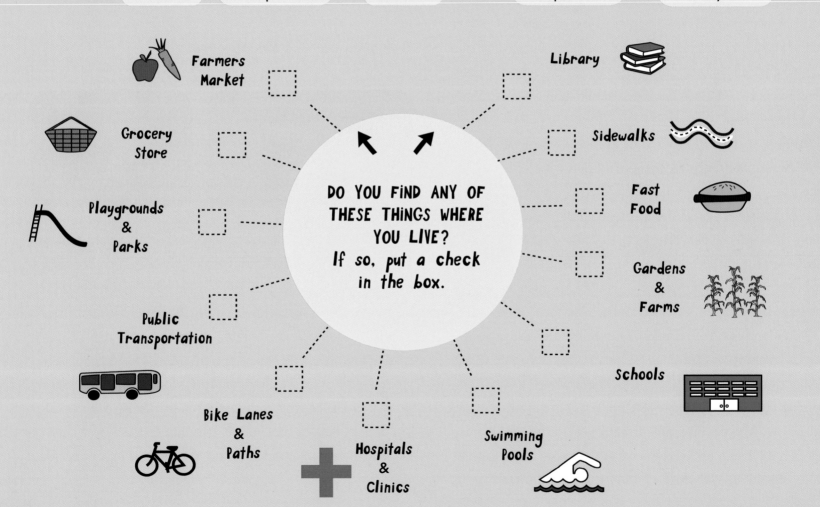

Farmers Market

Grocery Store

Playgrounds & Parks

Public Transportation

Bike Lanes & Paths

Library

Sidewalks

Fast Food

Gardens & Farms

Schools

Swimming Pools

Hospitals & Clinics

DO YOU FIND ANY OF THESE THINGS WHERE YOU LIVE?
If so, put a check in the box.

MAP MY NEIGHBORHOOD

Draw a map of your neighborhood below and try to include the things you checked on the last page. To start, draw where you live in the circle.

Put a star ☆ next to the things that help make people healthier!

MY HOME

way? (Check out the glossary on page 96 for more about what these terms mean.) These are questions we shouldn't be afraid to ask of our local suppliers. Request that a store stock more of the sort of food we really want to be eating and encourage them to buy local by promising to buy the local food they stock.

If we find ourselves living in a food desert, is there anything we can do about it besides driving miles from home to find higher quality alternatives? Yes. Check out the sidebar here on Urban Agriculture, as well as www.JustFood

.org, and there are lots of other local websites and blogs devoted to these subjects too (See selected resources on page 100.) The "Map Your Neighborhood" activity on pages

Growing Food Closer to Home

Of course, when it comes to fresh, healthy food, there is nothing better than being able to grow it yourself. Whether it's in a community garden or a kitchen pot, growing food closer to home guarantees freshness. John Ameroso, a passionate and lifelong gardener, has been doing this for more than thirty years in conjunction with other food organizations. In 1976 Ameroso took a vacant, rubble-filled lot in Brooklyn and transformed it into a community vegetable and flower garden. Since then he has cultivated gardens all over the city with an army of helpers, many of whom he's trained over the years. Last year, in one small section of the Bronx, eighteen tons of produce were grown and distributed to community residents. Ameroso and others also established East New York Farms!, which among other things, uses soil produced through composting to keep farm grounds fertile for growing collard, cilantro, chard, and many other vegetables.

21-22 is fun and instructive for people of all ages. Do it together as a family so that you can share your thoughts about what to eat and ways to get active. If you don't see what your community needs, make it happen with your friends and family. Start by asking questions. Get together with others and spread the word. Lesson learned: people need to know where farmers markets are so they can shop at them.

Edward's Destiny

Caleb and his family have gone through a lot. Caleb says that it's easier to make these changes knowing that what he's doing for himself is also improving the long-term outlook for his dad and his little brother. The three of them are doing it together. As they like to tell it, these days Edward—John's belly—is on death row.

Caleb and his family have found and created better food choices in their own neighborhood, but it is important to keep in mind that kids eat at least one meal a day at school. In some schools, the food isn't any better than what you can buy at a gas station or a fast food restaurant. Nationwide, school dining room staff, students, teachers, and parents are working for better school food options. In the next chapter, we'll join Safiyah and her family in a closer investigation of what kids are eating for lunch.

Caleb's Favorite Meatloaf

- ✔ 1 cup Italian bread crumbs (more if you'd like it more bready)
- ✔ 2 eggs
- ✔ 2½ lbs. lean ground turkey (2 packages)
- ✔ ⅔ cup parmesan cheese
- ✔ ⅓ cup nonfat milk (less if you like it more bready)
- ✔ ½ tsp fresh ground pepper (add more to taste)

Caleb's dad decided it was time to eat right! But that didn't mean he had to give up his favorite dishes. It just meant he had to change them around a bit.

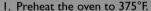

1. Preheat the oven to 375°F.
2. In a mixing bowl, combine breadcrumbs, ground turkey and eggs.
3. Add milk slowly until mixture is wet but not soupy.
4. Add ground pepper and parmesan cheese.
5. Mold into a 11×9×1-inch pan evening out mixture to 1 inch thick.
6. Bake in middle of oven for 35 minutes.
7. Let meatloaf sit for 5 minutes before serving.

Okra Gumbo

- ✔ 1 cup brown rice
- ✔ 1 cup vegetable stock
- ✔ 1 handful of fresh okra
- ✔ 1 red pepper, stemmed and diced
- ✔ 1 green pepper, stemmed and diced
- ✔ ½ tsp. cayenne pepper
- ✔ 1 clove finely chopped fresh garlic
- ✔ 1 teaspoon garlic powder
- ✔ ½ tsp. paprika
- ✔ 1 tsp. chili powder
- ✔ 1 pinch cumin
- ✔ 1 pinch basil
- ✔ 3 pinches parsley
- ✔ 1 pinch oregano
- ✔ ½ tsp. gumbo filé (you can find this in the seasoning section of your grocery store)

Inspired by a Creole Restaurant and Music Supper Club recipe found in *Go Green East Harlem*, edited by Manhattan Borough President Scott Stringer

1. In a small pot, add water, brown rice, ¼ cup vegetable stock, and bring to a boil. Simmer 40 minutes or until rice is soft.
2. Wash fresh okra and cut into ½ inch pieces. Place okra in a small pot of boiling water, cook for 30 seconds, remove and drain.
3. In a large skillet, add ⅛ cup of vegetable stock, cooked okra, green and red peppers, and cook over medium heat until mix becomes fragrant. Transfer to a small pot.
4. Add remaining vegetable stock to pot and bring to boil. While stirring, add all spices except gumbo filé.
5. Continue to stir, cook until okra is golden brown, and then add gumbo filé.
6. Cook for 10 minutes longer and serve on brown rice.
7. Enjoy time with your friends!

Sautéed Jalapeño Corn

- ✓ coarse sea salt
- ✓ 1 Tbs. extra-virgin olive oil
- ✓ 1 clove garlic, minced
- ✓ ½ tsp. ground cumin
- ✓ 3 cups fresh sweet corn, (from about 6 ears)
- ✓ 2 jalapeños, seeded and minced
- ✓ freshly ground white pepper

1. Bring 2 quarts of water and 2 teaspoons of salt to a boil in a medium pot.
2. Add the corn and immediately remove from stove. Let sit for 30 seconds and drain.
3. In a medium pan over medium heat, combine the olive oil, garlic, cumin, and ¼ teaspoon salt. Sauté, stirring often, until fragrant, about 2 minutes.
4. Add the corn and jalapeño to pan and cook, stirring frequently, until thoroughly mixed, 3 to 5 minutes.
5. Season with salt and white pepper to taste.

Inspired by a recipe from
Vegan Soul Kitchen
by Bryant Terry

Banana Coconut Cookies

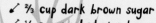

- ✓ ⅔ cup dark brown sugar
- ✓ ½ cup mashed ripe banana
- ✓ 1 cup lowfat plain yogurt
- ✓ 1 tsp. rum flavor
- ✓ ¾ cup all-purpose flour
- ✓ 1 cup quick-cooking oats
- ✓ ½ cup sweet flaked coconut
- ✓ ½ cup golden raisins
- ✓ ½ cup finely chopped walnuts
- ✓ 1 tsp. baking powder
- ✓ ⅛ tsp. ground nutmeg
- ✓ ¼ tsp. ground cinnamon
- ✓ dash of ground ginger

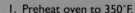

1. Preheat oven to 350°F.
2. In a large bowl, mix sugar, banana, yogurt and rum flavor, beating well until blended
3. Combine flour and remaining ingredients in a separate bowl, stirring with a whisk.
4. Add flour mixture by cup slowly to banana mixture.
5. Drop dough by 2-tablespoonfuls onto parchment-paper-lined baking sheet.
6. Bake at 350°F for 20 minutes or until edges of cookies are lightly browned.
7. Remove from oven and let cool completely.

Inspired by a recipe from the
Go Green East Harlem cookbook

Chapter Three

WHAT'S UP AT SCHOOL?

Safiyah, Kofa, Rachel, Tony

Sadie's best friend Safiyah lives with her mom Rachel, dad Tony, and younger brother Kofa. The whole family is vegetarian. Safiyah loves being vegetarian almost as much as she loves soccer, her favorite sport. She thinks it might be tougher to be a vegetarian family if they didn't have so many healthy food choices where they live on the Lower East Side. Her family doesn't eat out that often, but there are lots of good places for take-out when they don't want to cook.

One of Safiyah's favorite parts of the school day is lunch period. Although Safiyah and her brother always bring lunch from home to school, she was as curious as Sadie was when we started looking into where the school dining room was getting its menu ideas, how the food was prepared there, and where it all was coming from.

Digging In

Sadie and Safiyah began the **What's On YOUR Plate?** project by interviewing classmates at their public elementary school. They asked: What do you think about the food served in the dining room? Do you think it looks good? Do you think it tastes good? Do you eat the same thing every day? Do you bring food from home? The girls followed up by interviewing their principal. Then it was on to the school dietician, to find out more about the process of putting together a school menu. They learned that their school doesn't have a working stove. It had broken more than two years ago and was never replaced. A combination of bureaucracy, new equipment requirements and budget prevented concerned parents or teachers from speeding up the process. We were told it's on the "five-year plan."

For lunches, the school has to rely on what comes frozen and can be cooked or thawed in the microwave, or on foods that can be refrigerated and served quickly before they go bad. In the meantime, parents have banded together to see if we can come up with at least a temporary solution, such as raising enough money to buy the school a large rice cooker. We might even try helping our kids prepare their own meals by becoming "solar chefs," using inexpensive cookers powered by the sun that require no other energy.

School Lunch

Every day in the U.S., over 30 million kids eat lunches that are made in their school dining rooms, and many schools are required to offer their students breakfast. Some even offer dinner as part of their after-school programs. School meals can be the majority of a kid's daily nutrition, especially for lower-income families or for kids whose parents work long, inflexible hours. It's at school that kids are learning how to eat, which unfortunately means they're often learning to eat fast, cramming something down before the lunch "hour" (usually more like twenty minutes) is over. They learn to eat highly processed foods and to think it's natural that eating produces mountains of trash in the form of packaging, Styrofoam trays, plastic utensils.

One of the most telling things about the school lunch

program is that whether kids live in the plains, near the ocean or in the mountains, they're all eating the same things for lunch: subsidized frozen corn products in the form of fried mozzarella sticks, chicken nuggets and beef patties on processed white bread with government surplus cheese and a carton of non-organic whole milk.

Baby Steps Together

As they say, "Necessity is the mother of invention." We make do with what we have and that dictates what we can do. We take baby steps to find our way around a bureaucratic, underfunded, broken system responsible for feeding most of the children in this country. And we have to work together to make change happen.

Safiyah and Sadie found that getting to know the dining room staff makes them feel that we are all part of a team, a community with a shared mission: to help kids grow into healthy adults. The word "cafeteria" sounds so clinical, not like a place where a kid would want to hang out. So let's change that: let's call it the school dining room, and call the "lunch ladies" or "cafeteria workers" something more descriptive of how important their role really is. As others have suggested, we could call them "lunch teachers." Lunch teachers are an important part of the effort to fix school food nationwide. Together with parents, students and other teachers, they're party of the growing movement to overhaul what's on our trays.

Who Is Mrs. Q?

School lunch programs are a hot button issue on blogs, in books, and even on prime-time network television. One teacher in the Midwest, known only as Mrs. Q, created a popular blog called "Fed Up with Lunch: The School Lunch Project" (www.fedupwithschoollunch.blogspot .com). She decided to take a first-hand, undercover look at her school's food program by eating school lunch side by side with the kids on every school day of 2010 and then blogging about it. She has written passionately about "bagel dogs," "popcorn chicken," "sporks" (plastic utensils that take the place of silverware), heat-resistant packaging and many other aspects of school lunch today. She takes pictures of the more and less appetizing entrees and posts them on her site.

Mrs. Q is getting surprisingly attached to a few school lunch specialties such as the chicken teriyaki with rice and the burrito. But overall she's found that what's being served today—even with all the talk and legislation about serving fresher, healthier foods in our schools—is much less healthy than when she was in school. After eating her first 100 meals,

she said without doubt that the United States Department of Agriculture (USDA) has some "very warped" guidelines that result in tater tots and French fries being counted as vegetables, cookies counting in the "grain" category, things like frozen juice bars and fruit Jell-O counting as servings of fruit, and a full 95% of the food served to kids in her school going straight from freezer to microwave. There are few fresh foods, and a lot of unrecognizable non-food food items, which even a quick glance can tell you are full of fat, salt, and other ingredients that don't belong in a nutritious lunch.

Mrs. Q understands how tough it is for schools to fight against food supply chain restrictions, predatory marketing, fast food franchises near school grounds, and all the other obstacles to getting good school food to kids like Safiyah. But she also knows things have to change if we are going to reverse the declining health of our kids. So who's accountable?

Sadie and Safiyah Ask Around

In New York, Sadie and Safiyah realized their dining room dietician and their principal had their hands tied as far as what they can serve, where they can get it from and, of course, how much they have to spend. They're restricted by budget and also by the policies of the NYC Department of Education and the USDA. So our Nancy Drews decided to go to the top: they spoke with Chef Jorge Collazo and Chief Executive Eric

Goldstein, who run the school lunch programs for all of New York City.

Chef Jorge and Eric spoke with Sadie and Safiyah about how they plan the menus for the second largest feeding program in the country, outside of the US Military. They explained that they have to strike the right balance between making sure kids don't go hungry and ensuring that they are served healthy, nutritious foods. They have to do it all on a strict budget and in a way that is safe, fair, and equal across all their school districts. So, while they want to feed kids fresh foods that are healthy, they're up against a huge bureaucracy. Also, because of the popular assumption that kids won't eat certain foods even if they are fresh and good for them, they put a premium on offering foods that are "appetizing," which at times translates into offering bagels instead of yogurt or chicken nuggets instead of skinless, grilled chicken.

The NYC school food program has a herculean task—there's no question about it. And the school system isn't only tasked with serving meals during the school year: over the summer vacation, the city makes free lunches available to any person under eighteen at many facilities, including schools,

CAFETERIA SNOOPS

What's happening in your school's dining room?

Profile someone who works In your school's dining room

At your next lunch period, ask someone who works there if you could interview them. There may be a time of day that they are really busy and another time that they would like to host a visitor, like after school.

Name:
_____

What do you like to eat at home?
_____

What was school lunch like when you were growing up?
_____

What's something you like about our school's dining room?
_____

What's one thing you would like to change about our school's dining room?
_____

DRAW OR PASTE A PICTURE OF
YOUR INTERVIEWEE HERE

Interview Your Lunchroom Staff

Now interview your lunchroom staff about your school's kitchen. Come up with two of your own questions!

- Where does the food come from?

- Who decides the menu?

- How many meals are prepared each day?

- How are the meals prepared?

- Do you use a stove? Microwave? Grill? Hot plate?

- What kinds of foods do you buy?

- Are there any local foods?

- What is the most popular item on the menu?

- What's your favorite item on the menu?

- (Your Question #1)

- (Your Question #2)

Investigate Your School

Take a walk around your school to find out how it is doing with health, nutrition and the environment.

How many vending machines are there in school?

Do they sell soda and candy?

How many times a week do you have gym class?

Do you have recess everyday? For how long?

Do you have plastic or reuseable utensils?

What are your lunch trays made of?

Are there places to buy fast food and candy near your school? How many?

What kinds of treats do you have in class?

parks and public pools throughout NYC. Despite all the attention and effort, 40% of NYC's public school students are obese, and what is being served for breakfast and lunch in school is often adding to the problem.

Sadie and Safiyah asked Chef Jorge and Eric why they allow Snapple in vending machines given its high sugar content. Eric responded that, "A lot of schools used to have soda machines, so we moved to juice and water (in the vending machines)—you don't have to buy a Snapple. We give out milk with our meals." Safiyah didn't miss a beat: "I know it's not your fault," she told him, "but when the kid sees some Snapple and some milk, the kid's gonna want the juice." Chef Jorge added that Snapple is "100% fruit juice. At least it's a healthier option than a lot of other school districts are offering." However, the girls found out that for all its efforts to market itself as a healthy alternative to soda, Snapple actually contains more sugar than Coca-Cola, and often uses the least nutritious and most inexpensive fruit concentrates in its drinks.

Really, it had more to do with money than with health. Eric explained that the Snapple machines pay for the sports programs. Snapple won a bid to become the exclusive beverage provider in NYC schools by promising the school system an $8 million profit per year on school sales of its beverages. Connecting the dots, the girls said, "But you can't run on empty calories."

When Safiyah and Sadie ask questions, it shows consumers—even kids—that you don't have to take everything

you're told at face value. We all have a right and duty to understand why certain decisions are being made. Obviously, Sadie and Safiyah didn't get all the answers they were looking for in that interview. But by asking their questions, they got the ball rolling. It helps Chef Jorge and Eric to see that it's not just parents: kids aren't happy with this situation either.

Good News

They've instituted salad bars in many of the schools, which kids seem to like a lot. Safiyah says, "Salad bars are fun to use, you get to choose, you get to make your own lunch and that makes you feel like you have a little more independence. It makes you feel privileged." The school system has replaced white bread with wheat. They're offering kids fresh fruits and vegetables, whether whole or sliced in packages. Low-fat milk has been substituted for whole, and recently they have started offering whole-wheat pasta dishes. In general, Chef Jorge and Eric want to offer kids more choices.

Peanut butter and jelly sandwiches date back to World War II when the army supplied troops with rations of both peanut butter and jelly, and soldiers cleverly combined the two on slices of bread. Back in the U.S.A., PB&J became a hit. Today many kids in the U.S. will eat over 1,500 PB&J sandwiches before they graduate from high school.

PB & J sandwiches

Not all PB&J sandwiches are created equal!
Take a look at how these two different PB&Js match up.

Ordinary PB&J

Exceptional PB&J

Ordinary PB&J		
Bread	(−)	Sliced white bread, NO FIBER, NO PROTEIN
	(−)	Made by removing all the natural wheat fiber.
	(−)	May have High Fructose Corn Syrup.
Jelly	(−)	Contains no real fruit!
	(−)	2 tablespons have 6 teaspoons sugar—about the same as half a can of soda.
	(−)	Contains High Fructose Corn Syrup.
Peanut Butter	(−)	Brands like Jif, Skippy and Peter Pan
	(−)	Sugar added! Often it is the second ingredient.
	(−)	May have High Fructose Corn Syrup.
	(−)	Ingredients include: corn syrup solids, sugar and soy protein, and hydrogenated vegetable oils.

Exceptional PB&J		
Bread	(+)	Sliced whole grain bread
	(+)	2 slices contain 6 ounces of fiber.
	(+)	No sugar added
Jelly	(+)	All natural fruit preserves
	(+)	Contains real fruit.
Peanut Butter	(+)	Ingredients: peanuts, salt
	(+)	Packed with healthy protein.
	(+)	Made by crushing peanuts—that's it!
	(+)	No preservatives
	(+)	No sugar added
	(+)	No trans fats

More To Chew On

Whether kids eat school food or like Safiyah, bring food from home, they face many of the same issues. Besides nutrition,

there's the schedule and waste management. All students are affected by the length of the lunch period. Although Safiyah loves apples, she didn't used to have time to finish hers. She was racing to get outside for recess. But parents and the principal worked together to reposition recess before lunch. Kids are eating more and better foods and not rushing through.

When it comes to waste, whether we're throwing away the styrofoam trays we put our lunches on or the plastic bags we brought our sandwiches in, we're all making too much trash. One study found that the typical American kid generates 67 pounds of discarded school lunch packaging waste in a single year, adding up to a whopping 18,000 pounds yearly for the average elementary school. That's a lot of plastic utensils, plastic bags, paper napkins, and juice boxes. What's the alternative?

Let's put on our thinking caps and get creative. Brainstorm with other kids and parents at your school about ways you can make school lunches healthier and more fun. What about kids joining in the meal preparation? Growing some food for the kitchen to serve? Taking a nutrition class? Designing and posting daily menus which makes lunchtime a celebration of the good meals being served? Maybe serve some meals family style, at communal tables? Encourage each other to get to know the school dieticians and the other lunch teachers so that we can all learn to play an active role in maintaining our own health.

We can all do what Mrs. Q, Sadie and Safiyah, and the parents at the Neighborhood School are doing. We have to engage other kids and other parents, and forge real bonds with the staffs of our schools. There are a lot of cool ideas out there. We have neighbors, friends, family, local, state and federal officials, school administrators who are ready to join with us. Let's roll up our sleeves and get to work.

In the next chapter, we'll meet a young boy named Gabriel who has a variety of food-related medical challenges. He'll show us how he navigates meals at school and at home.

Was There Always School Lunch?

In the United States, school lunches were not always something that came automatically with classes and recess. In 1853, New York City kicked off the effort when the NYC branch of the Children's Aid Society started offering subsidized school lunches in some NYC schools.

For many years this program stayed small and was confined to parts of New York City. Then in 1904, an important book came out, which had a huge impact. *Poverty* by Robert Hunter focused on the plight of poor children in New York City. They were frequently showing up for school hungry and unable to concentrate on schoolwork because they didn't have the necessary nutrition and calories. He said that as a matter of principle, the government should "make full and adequate provision for the physical needs" of poor kids. At that time in the United States, it was estimated that there were two million school age kids who were going hungry.

Soon after that book came out, other cities, such as Philadelphia and Boston, began to adopt small school lunch programs that were funded by private sources or organizations like Children's Aid. The idea spread. In 1919, the NYC Board of Education formally assumed all responsibility for school lunches in Manhattan and the Bronx.

The problem of good nutrition and hunger got to be more pressing during WWII, when many young men and boys were being turned away from service because they were not healthy enough to serve. The federal government began to see nutrition as a national priority. In 1946 Congress passed the National School Lunch Act, which made school lunch programs "permanent and integral to school systems," calling them measures of "national security," designed to "safeguard the health and well-being of the nation's children." In 1966, President Johnson signed into law the Child Nutrition Act, which further expanded this effort. It also established school breakfast programs, which now feed an additional 10 million kids a day.

It's ironic that the national school lunch program was launched at a time when students were not being fed enough to be capable of defending their country, because today 27% of all young adults who try to enlist in the military are turned away, deemed "Too Fat to Fight." That's the name of a report released in 2010. This statistic increased by 70% in just thirteen years. The report has sounded an alarm, concluding that obesity is a national security issue. Not having enough military personnel deemed fit for service is one risk the country does not want to take. Just as in the 1940s when the national school lunch program was necessary to keep young people healthy and strong, today we face a similar challenge but in reverse. It is not to make sure we have enough calories, but that we don't have too many. They can't be empty calories, and we must be given the chance to burn them off.

Caprese Salad

- ✓ 2 large tomatoes
- ✓ 1 lb. fresh mozzarella
- ✓ 12 large basil leaves
- ✓ coarse sea salt
- ✓ freshly ground white pepper
- ✓ extra-virgin olive oil

Simple is good. Caprese salad only has a few ingredients but the tastes combine so perfectly, you would think you were eating a complex concoction.

1. Cut tomatoes into thick slices.
2. Cut the fresh mozzarella into slices. Place a mozzarella slice on top of each tomato slice. Put a basil leaf on top of each stack.
3. Sprinkle salt and pepper over the top of the tomatoes and mozzarella slices and drizzle extra-virgin olive oil and serve immediately.

Cheeseless Pizza

Pizza Dough
- ✓ 1 pkg. active dry yeast
- ✓ ⅔ cup warm water
- ✓ 1 tsp. honey
- ✓ 1 tsp. salt
- ✓ 4 cup whole wheat flour
- ✓ 1 Tbs. honey
- ✓ 3 Tbs. olive oil
- ✓ ⅔ cup warm water

Topping Options
- ✓ Tomato sauce
- ✓ Sliced eggplant
- ✓ Olives, pitted
- ✓ Sliced tomatoes
- ✓ Mushrooms
- ✓ Spinach
- ✓ Peppers

Experiment with your favorite ingredients to make your own variation on this cheeseless pizza.

1. Preheat oven to 350°F.
2. In a small bowl, mix first 3 ingredients. Let stand for 5 minutes until foamy.
3. In a large bowl, combine salt, flour (no need to use the full quantity—use enough flour to make a stiff dough), honey, oil, and the second ⅔ cup warm water.
4. Mix together yeast and flour mixture and knead on a lightly floured surface until smooth and elastic.
5. Place dough into an oiled bowl and turn once to coat with oil. Cover and let rise until doubled in size (about 45 minutes to 1 hour).
6. Sprinkle a pan with cornmeal or semolina flour. Press dough out with a rolling pin (or kid's hands) into a circle. You may need to use more flour to keep dough from sticking.
7. Brush with olive oil and spread with your favorite toppings.
8. Bake for 15–20 minutes or until edges of dough are golden.

Apple Crumble

Fruit
- ✓ 2 lbs. favorite variety apples
- ✓ 1 lemon, juiced
- ✓ ¼ cup sugar in the raw
- ✓ 1 Tbs. cornstarch or flour

Topping
- ✓ ¾ cup rolled oats
- ✓ ¾ cup whole wheat flour
- ✓ ½ cup sugar in the raw
- ✓ ⅓ cup butter, softened
- ✓ ½ tsp. cinnamon
- ✓ ½ tsp. allspice
- ✓ 2 tsp. vanilla extract

Inspired by a recipe from
www.lightheartedlocavore.com

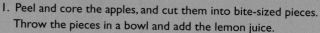

1. Peel and core the apples, and cut them into bite-sized pieces. Throw the pieces in a bowl and add the lemon juice.
2. In different bowl, a small one, mix the raw sugar and the corn starch or flour. Sprinkle that mixture over the fruit, toss gently to coat the apples. Move the apples to the baking dish.
3. For the topping, combine the oats, flour, sugar, cinnamon, allspice and vanilla together. Stir in the butter and mix until everything comes together with a doughy texture. Sprinkle this evenly over the fruit.
4. Place the baking dish in the oven on the middle rack, and bake at 350°F until the topping begins to brown, which should be about 20–25 minutes.
5. Throw some ice cream on top, or whipped cream, or just eat it straight. It'll be delicious warm or at room temperature. Very delicious.

Safiyah's Tofu Scramble

- ✓ 1 block firm tofu
- ✓ ½ onion, finely chopped
- ✓ ⅓ cup sliced mushrooms
- ✓ ½ green, yellow or red pepper, chopped
- ✓ 1 celery stalk, chopped
- ✓ 4 garlic cloves, pressed
- ✓ 2 Tbs. nutritional yeast (optional)
- ✓ 1 tsp. turmeric
- ✓ 1 tsp. chili powder (more or less to taste)
- ✓ 1 tsp. cumin
- ✓ olive oil
- ✓ salt and pepper

Tofu for breakfast!

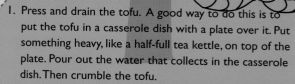

1. Press and drain the tofu. A good way to do this is to put the tofu in a casserole dish with a plate over it. Put something heavy, like a half-full tea kettle, on top of the plate. Pour out the water that collects in the casserole dish. Then crumble the tofu.
2. Put olive oil in a large frying pan over medium heat. Cook the onion for a few minutes until soft.
3. Add the tofu, mushrooms, pepper, celery, garlic, cumin, turmeric, and chili powder. Turn down the heat, and cook for 5–7 more minutes. Keep stirring and add more olive oil as needed.
4. Taste it. Add nutritional yeast, salt and pepper, and more cumin if you like. Cumin really makes this dish come alive.
5. Serve with warm tortillas and salsa.

Chapter Four

WHAT DOES YOUR BODY NEED?

Waldo, Gabriel, Dario, Cathy, Dahlia

At Sadie and Safiyah's elementary school, we met Gabriel who's ten and his eight-year old brother Dario. They live with their parents, Cathy Albisa and Waldo Cubero, in Manhattan. Cathy is a Cuban-American who grew up in Miami and came to New York in 1986. She met Waldo in Cuba in 1998, and he immigrated the following year. Both grew up eating traditional Cuban food—lots of rice, beans, fried plantains, pork, avocados, and tropical fruit. Both of them found New York to be a food adventure, where they learned to eat food from every continent and planned their weekends around which cuisine to explore. After the kids were born, though, it was back to cooking every night. In 2003, Gabriel's grandmother came from Cuba to live with them. She is diabetic and faces enormous difficulty controlling her sugar levels, so when she arrived it was time to throw all the sweets out of the house.

Experimenting with Alternatives

When Gabriel was born, his mom started slowly educating herself about food and nutrition—something to which she had previously paid little attention. Gabriel and his brother were both breastfed until they were three (in tandem for one year!), and for the first year of each of their lives, their parents only bought organic fruits and vegetables for them to eat. Cathy still hadn't learned about the way livestock was raised and its impact on health, so they bought the least expensive factory-farmed beef. Buying organic was an economic challenge because Waldo was a stay at home dad and Cathy works at a non-profit, so beyond feeding the kids some organic produce, pricier food seemed out of reach.

When Gabriel was three and a half, he developed asthma and had terrible eczema, especially in the winter. When Gabriel was four, he was diagnosed with dyslexia. His mother went into research mode, learning everything she could about the issue and she discovered the profound link between learning disabilities and nutrition. Around that time, his brother began to manifest sensory integration problems, which is also a developmental disability. Dario faced some learning issues as well. At this point, the entire household changed its nutritional profile. Sustainable meat, locally grown fruits

What's the Dirt?

One in three U.S. children born in the year 2000 could develop type 2 diabetes during their lifetimes.

and vegetables, organic dairy, fish oils, probiotics, and whole grains became a way of life.

Despite these efforts, Gabriel often felt sick and suffered mild digestive trouble. His doctor determined that he had a milk allergy, and his mom proceeded to eliminate all dairy from his diet. (In solidarity, his parents gave up dairy as well, except for milk in the sacred morning cups of *café con leche*.) Adjusting to a dairy-free, organic, sustainable, local foods kitchen was not an easy change. Waldo could no longer pick up groceries at the convenient bodega on the corner. Instead, he had to trek around the city, shopping at the few places where healthy food was available for Gabriel and for the whole family.

The prices were not easy to stomach either, but fortunately by this time, Gabriel's dad had been re-certified as a dentist in this country and started working again. By now, Gabriel and his brother were thriving. Gabriel had not only learned to read but actually loved reading and was devouring books. Dario had a rough start at school in pre-k and Kindergarten, but by first grade most of his sensory issues had resolved and he was in a classroom he loved.

Diabetes in the Family

One morning last year, I noticed Gabriel and his mom in the school hallway. She had tears streaming down her cheeks—which was totally out of character. Gabriel's blood sugar had shot up for three days in a row while he had a cold, and the doctors worried he might be developing juvenile diabetes. This would leave him unable to produce any insulin at all. It would mean he'd have to give himself insulin shots several times a day for the rest of his life. Cathy was trying desperately to make sense out of what the doctors told her, the information she'd found online, and the experiences of other parents and children at the school.

When the tests came back from the diabetes center,

though, he didn't have any of the antibodies normally associated with juvenile diabetes, an autoimmune disease that produces these antibodies. The doctor was flummoxed and recommended a wait-and-see approach. A year later, his blood sugar is still normal but his parents worry that every time he gets sick he can't produce enough insulin to keep his blood sugar normal. Now they watch his diet even more vigilantly. Since the doctors can't guarantee that he won't develop the antibodies, his parents want at least to make sure that his diet doesn't contribute to the risk.

Type 1 is the category of diabetes that used to be referred to as "juvenile diabetes," but now it is also common among adults. Nobody's quite sure why this type of diabetes occurs, though it seems to have a lot of genetic factors, and some suspect that it may have environmental, dietary, or viral causes as well. What's known for certain is that there isn't a cure—yet. The only way to manage blood sugar levels is through insulin, coupled with a diet regimen and exercise.

With the long-term complications that may arise from this disease, including serious problems with the eyes, kidneys, nervous, and cardiovascular system, it's no wonder Gabriel's mom was so upset that morning at school.

Gabriel's family has a history of diabetes. His great-grandmother died of type 2 diabetes in her fifties, and his grandmother, Dalia, also has type 2. Although she doesn't exercise as much as is recommended, Dalia does avoid white sugar. She tends to drink diet soda and loves sugar-free cookies. Unfortunately, these cookies are made up almost entirely of white flour, which diabetics should avoid. Because Dalia doesn't give herself the care that she shows her family and

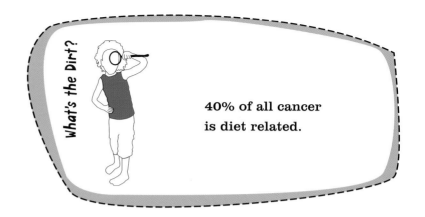

What's the Dirt?

40% of all cancer is diet related.

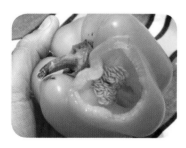

friends, Gabriel and the rest of the family encourage her to take better care of herself. Type 2 diabetes can produce serious long-term health complications;, however with a commitment to better nutrition, a rigorous diet, and a regular workout regimen, the disease doesn't have to keep getting worse.

Type 2 diabetes used to be a disease that people developed in their 30s or 40s or when they were older, so it was referred to as "adult onset diabetes." In 1994, only 5% of all cases of diabetes in kids were cases of type 2 diabetes, and the rest were type 1 diabetes. Today, 20% of all incidences of diabetes in kids are classified as type 2. Type 2 diabetes in children and young adults is much more common among African Americans, Latinos, and Native Americans. Of young adults diagnosed with type 2, 80% are overweight, and 40% are classified as clinically obese. It's clear that the obesity epidemic in the U.S. and the dramatic increase in type 2 diabetes among young adults and kids are closely connected

GUESS THE GRAPH

Are we healthier than we were 40 years ago?
It depends on how you measure it . . .

The graph below has 4 lines that show changes over the last 40 years in:

the % of adults who are overweight or obese
the % of children who are overweight or obese
the % of people who wear seatbelts regularly
the % of adults who smoke

Can you guess which line shows which change?

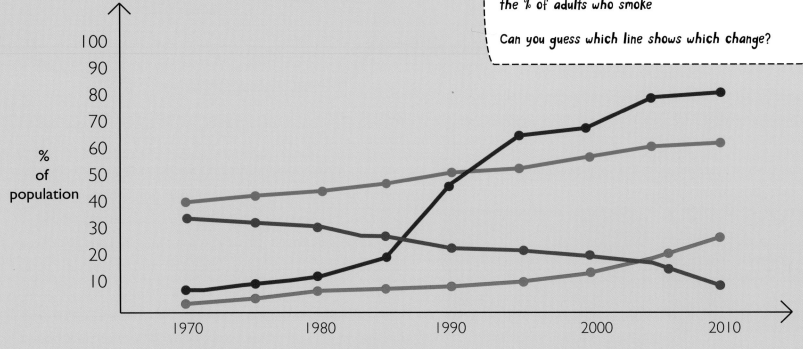

Year by decade

Can you guess which line shows: Circle One:

% of adults who are overweight or obese
% of children who are overweight or obese
% of people who wear seatbelts regularly
% of adults who smoke

CONNECT THE YEARS

Which muscle never stops working your entire life?
Follow history from 1930 until today to find out!

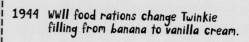

1930 First dedicated Soup Kitchen opens in Chicago.

1944 WWII food rations change Twinkie filling from banana to vanilla cream.

1946 US President Harry Truman signs the National School Lunch Act.

1953 Frozen packaged meals trademarked as "TV Dinners"

1962 4% obesity in kids ages 6-11

1964 Doritos first launched nationally

1965 Food and Agricultural Act signed (first Farm Bill)

1967 First popular home microwave sold in appliance stores

1976 Big Gulp first sold as 32 oz at 7-Eleven

1977 High Fructose Corn Syrup begins to be added to packaged foods.

1980 5% obesity in kids ages 6-11

1988 7-Eleven increases Big Gulp to 64 oz.

1990 Organic Food Production Act is passed. requiring the USDA to develop national standards for organic food.

1994 Nutrition Labeling and Education Act of 1990 authorizes FDA to require Nutrition Facts labels.

2001 25% of meals eaten in the U.S. are fast food.

2008 19.6% obesity in kids ages 6-11

2009 The number of farmers markets in the US passes 5,000.

Today you make a change in your diet!

phenomena. The White House Task Force on Obesity comes at a crucial time in this crisis. Elected officials, school lunch administrators, medical professionals, children, and parents alike are working to stem this tide.

Gabriel's doctor was sure, despite the lack of anti-bodies for type 1 that he couldn't have type 2. When Cathy asked how the doctor could be so sure, she said, "His blood work shows he's way too healthy to have that." So some of these changes were paying off! The doctor also said, he might just be a "low producer"—someone who has trouble producing enough insulin to regulate his blood sugar. This made his mother very conscious of avoiding refined foods that might put a strain on his pancreas (the organ that produces insulin) and deepened her commitment to a more natural diet for him.

Gabriel's Plate

Gabriel's family rarely eats out, twice a month at most. Gabriel's favorite food at the moment is shrimp, but Dario says shrimp gives him a headache. Dario's favorite food is a home-made burger, but Gabriel doesn't like burgers! Neither boy

likes vegetables very much, but they both like fruit. When they shop, they have to go out of their way to find beef that is grass-fed, salmon that is marine-certified, and olive oil that is cold-pressed. And these preferences are more expensive. The family is on a budget, yet Cathy and Waldo have prioritized the more expensive, healthier, organic options.

Gabriel loves his traditional Cuban cuisine. He eats rice with most meals, but doesn't like the nuttiness of the healthier brown rice. Cathy keeps trying different ways of preparing brown rice since it would be healthier for everyone. (White rice has had the inner husk—or bran—removed and often glucose is used to polish the grain, which results in the loss of nutrients and dietary fiber.) Gabriel loves his beans, especially black beans, which are really good for him because they're packed with protein, vitamins, iron, and fiber. Seafood plays a huge role in his meals, as do tropical fruits of all kinds, especially mangoes, papayas, and plantains. Mojo sauce, which is made of oil, garlic, onion, spices, and lime juice, is a staple, especially on holidays when pork is always served. A variety of stews and soups frequently appear on the menu.

His brother, on the other hand, is the picky eater in the family. Like many kids, he's especially sensitive about the textures of food. He would choose to live on peanut butter and jelly sandwiches. (See Tale of Two PB&J Sandwiches on page 34.) Gabriel is the happy assistant chef for his dad Waldo who does most of the cooking in the family. They tend to make large meals with leftovers to last for days. One of the family's go-to meals consists of free-range, organic chicken mixed with fresh tomato sauce, potatoes and onions. (See recipe

for Chicken with Spices on page 49.) Sometimes they make paella, adding surprise ingredients they discover in the fridge.

Food plays a huge role in the family's weekends since on weeknights Waldo gets home from work too late to eat with the others and Dalia prefers to eat her meals in front of the TV, a habit the family is trying to get her to break. On Saturdays, Gabriel loves going with his mom to the farmers market and bringing back an assortment of ripe, sweet fruits, and whatever else looks good. After they recover from running around doing errands, Gabriel and his family spend the rest of Sunday at home cooking, eating, and hanging out.

Both boys love dessert, but that has to be limited. On weeknights, they are allowed a dessert of no more than 70 or so calories. But on weekends, Gabriel and Waldo prepare their special dairy-free cake, which everyone has a slice of on Sunday morning. Once a week, the boys are allowed to go to the local vegan ice cream shop for a treat. On weekdays, Dario and Gabriel have whole wheat bread, but they are allowed to have white bread on the weekends. It's not easy for Cathy or Waldo. They are always trying to teach their kids what is healthy, but they get a lot of push back. They have to say "no" a lot.

While Cathy, Waldo, Gabriel, Dario, and Dalia face challenges, they are not alone as they continue to investigate better foods, regimes and good habits. More attention is being paid to the link between children's diets and their health, which is something we all benefit from. As we have seen earlier, Sadie, with the help of our family, doctors and the internet,

What's So Bad About SUGAR Anyway?

When my son Kofi was a tiny baby, I started calling him "Sugar." The nickname has stuck because—as I see it—he's sweeter than honey. He also has a cousin called Sugar, and two aunts who call everyone Sugar, and most of his friends realize that "Shoog" is short for Kofi.

However, when we talk about sugar in food, we generally mean a processed white, crystalline, unnatural substance that has very little to do with the sugar cane plant it started out as. Sugar cane or sugar beets are put through a series of industrial processes that refine it down to pure sucrose after stripping away all the vitamins, minerals, proteins, enzymes, and other beneficial nutrients it naturally contains. This leaves behind a concentrated, chemical substance the body isn't able to process or digest easily.

Sugar is not only bad for our teeth, but it may increase the risk of diabetes, hypo- and hyperglycemia, heart disease, and, many believe, mental illness and depression. It increases hyperactivity in kids and produces irritability and anxiety, not to mention weight gain. When consumed over the long term, it has negative effects on the pancreas, adrenal glands, and the endocrine systems.

On average, people in the United States consume 115 pounds of refined sugar each year. This begins in the very first days of life if they are given certain infant formulas, and even through breast milk if the mother has refined sugar in her own diet. Many of us may be addicted to refined sugar.

Sweet people in our lives are much healthier for us than refined sugar. See where you can eat less of it—or get it out of your diet all together. Side affects to ousting refined sugar may include: a more fit body, a less stressed mind, better grades, clearer skin, a longer life, happiness, and peace in the world. The list could go on.

has figured out how to manage her cholesterol through diet, and Caleb and Jojo, with the help of their dad, coaches, and farmers market managers are on a better track to avoiding heart disease. In the following chapter, we'll meet Lizbeth Angel whose family can maintain their farm because of the increased demand for fresh and healthy food. These are all examples of how a healthy, active food chain can be a chain of good habits.

Classic Black Beans

- ✓ 1 pkg. black beans
- ✓ water
- ✓ oregano
- ✓ 1 white or yellow onion
- ✓ olive oil
- ✓ 1 tsp. sugar
- ✓ 1 dash salt
- ✓ 1 green pepper, chopped

Some like 'em spicy. Add as much red pepper as you like.

1. Soak beans overnight with about three quarters of an inch of water over where the beans end.
2. Sauté oregano, onions in olive oil.
3. Add sautéed onions to the beans.
4. In a pressure cooker, add a small teaspoon of sugar, salt, a little more olive oil, and green pepper—then just turn the pressure cooker on.
5. If you do not have a pressure cooker, put all ingredients in a large pot and cook covered over low to medium heat.
6. When finished, serve with anything; our favorite is brown rice and salad.

Chicken with Potatoes and Spices

- ✓ 4–6 free-range, organic chicken parts (breasts, legs, wings, whatever you like best)
- ✓ 2 cups fresh tomato sauce
- ✓ 3 small potatoes, peeled and roughly chopped
- ✓ 2 onions
- ✓ 4 small cloves peeled garlic
- ✓ 2 Tbs. olive oil
- ✓ 2 fresh sprigs of any available herbs; rosemary, thyme, oregano, and sage are all good and available in many regions and gardens.
- ✓ 1 tsp. paprika (and any other of your favorite spices to taste)
- ✓ 4 Tbs. lime juice (optional)

1. In large pot, brown chicken in olive oil.
2. Add onions, garlic and stir, cooking until onions are clear. Add potatoes, herbs, spices, tomato sauce and lime juice (optional) until all is covered.
3. Cook uncovered on medium heat until small bubbles rise to the top. Reduce heat and simmer on low for 30 minutes, or until chicken is thoroughly cooked and tender. You may need to add more tomato sauce or chicken broth to keep ingredients from going dry.
4. Serve with salad or over rice.

A spruced-up, spiced-up take on the traditional meat and potatoes dinner

Quick Granola

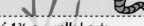

Granola is a great snack for afternoons after school.

- 1¾ cup rolled oats
- ¾ cup unsweetened coconut, toasted
- ½ tsp. salt
- ¼ tsp. ground cinnamon
- 2 tsp. unsalted butter
- 1¼ Tbs. canola oil
- 1 Tbs. honey
- 2¼ Tbs. maple syrup
- ¼ cup almonds, unsalted, whole, toasted
- ¼ cup pumpkin seeds, unsalted, toasted
- 1 Tbs. sunflower seeds, unsalted, toasted
- ¼ cup raisins
- 1 Tbs. golden raisins
- ¼ cup dried cherries
- 1 Tbs. dried apricot, small dice

1. Preheat oven to 350°F.
2. In a small saucepan, heat butter, oil, honey, and maple syrup to blend.
3. In a separate bowl, combine oats, coconut, salt and cinnamon.
4. Add the warm liquid ingredients to the oat mixture and mix until fully incorporated.
5. Spread the mixture evenly on a cookie sheet and bake for 30–45 minutes. If you raise the temperature, make sure to check frequently to keep the granola from burning. Remove from oven and cool.
6. Add toasted nuts and dried fruit and mix to incorporate. Store in an airtight container or freeze in bags.

Cathy's Leftover Kale Croquettes

- leftover salmon (or any other protein leftovers)
- bunch of fresh kale
- 3 cloves garlic
- 1 tsp. cumin
- 1 large onion
- 3 Tbs. flour
- 1 Tbs. of oil
- ½ cup water or milk
- 1 egg
- breadcrumbs

"One thing we make is croquettes from all kinds of leftover food." —Cathy

1. Take the leftover fish and whatever else you want and put them through a meat grinder.
2. Add cumin, garlic and onions to the fish and sauté it a bit.
3. Separately, add three tablespoons of flour and a tablespoon of oil to a pan over low heat and mix.
4. Slowly mix in the ½ cup of water or milk—because of the bad reaction my kids have to milk, I use water.
5. Add the fish and kale and mix that in slowly.
6. When the mix is no longer sticking to the pan, take it out.
7. Let it cool, then roll them into croquettes.
8. Roll in egg and flour or breadcrumbs and bake at 350°F for 10 minutes or until golden.

Chapter Five

WHO'S YOUR FARMER?

Henry, Lizbeth, Crisostomo, Ana, Maria, Jennifer, Oreo

Lizbeth Angel is a college student, architectural firm intern, and daughter of two Mexican immigrants, Ana and Chrisostomo Angel, who came to the United States in the late 80s. She has a teenage brother Henry and two little sisters, Jennifer and Maria.

Sadie and Safiyah introduced us to Lizbeth and her family. The three girls met when Lizbeth was working at NYC's Lower East Side Girls Club, which offers a space for girls and young women to learn leadership skills, get free prom dresses, sell fresh produce and baked goods, and interact with new friends and mentors in the community. After the girls told Lizbeth about the **What's On YOUR Plate?** project, she invited them over to see her family's seedlings in their backyard in Brooklyn.

A Mother's Dream

Lizbeth's mother, Ana, had mainly worked in a factory since coming to the United States. Her workplace looked nothing like the farm she had grown up on. Ana's father was a farmer in the south of Mexico raising cattle and crops of corn, beans and watermelon. She and her family loved living in Brooklyn, but she found herself missing the Mexican countryside—the mountains, chili peppers growing right outside her door, the way her family cultivated land, and the guacamole made fresh from avocados in the garden. She dreamed of having a farm of her own one day.

During Ana's early years in the United States, she was too busy raising a family, working long hours, and maintaining a household to take on anything as huge as starting a farm. But she kept the idea in the back of her mind. Occasionally she dis-

cussed it with Lizbeth's father but he wasn't convinced that farming would be "a good occupation for a woman." Then one day, they saw a television show that described a GrowNYC program called the New Farmer Development Project which supports farmers as they start out. Ana decided to apply. She says, "When I found this program I thought, 'I can have everything here. I can have the urban culture of my kids and my own culture, which is farming.'"

At first though, no one but Ana held out much hope that she would be accepted; while the program director was herself a woman, most everyone was pessimistic about the idea of a woman farmer and doubted that she'd be considered qualified. Ana's persistence and commitment was apparent in her application and she was accepted. She immediately found a plot of land to lease in upstate New York, and though nothing about the journey has been easy, she has never regretted following her dream.

A Family Affair

The Angels had a little experience in the food business before they became farmers. In 1992, they had a food stand at the water's edge in Brooklyn with a view of the Statue of Liberty in the distance. The Angels' food stand mainly served home-made tacos, featuring homemade corn tortillas filled with chicken, pork, cilantro, onions, tomatoes, avocado, green

tomatillos, and salsa picante. (See Tamales by Angels recipe on page 66.)

Between opening the taco stand and 2004, when Ana was first accepted into the farming program, the Angels, who live on the first floor of a small row house, were scrambling to make a living and to raise their children. Once Ana took on the farm, she realized that she would need the entire family's help and support to make it work. Soon, Lizbeth's dad left his restaurant job and starting working the farm with Ana in the high season. But to this day, like many farmers in the US, he has to find multiple, short-term jobs every winter to make ends meet.

Lizbeth and her brother also regularly work at the farm, where they help plant, maintain, and harvest the crops. This inspired Lizbeth to switch her school major to agriculture. The farm is a family business now, a true communal effort, and it's hard to tell who enjoys it the most. Everyone appreciates how it brings them closer—to each other and to their customers who get to buy fresh, healthy, locally grown food.

Industrialization

Farming—which has been called the original green job—has a long history going back more than 12,000 years when food crops were first intentionally cultivated, grown and harvested for human consumption. In the 20th century, the industrialization of agriculture was marked by the advent of synthetic fertilizer, petroleum-based pesticides, selective breeding and mechanization. Farming was transformed. When the US Farm Bill started subsidizing commodity production in 1965, (see Farm Bill sidebar on page 64.) certain crops, like corn, wheat and cotton—and their largest producers—were given the most support. By 2009, 10% of farmers received 74% of all the subsidies. In the same year, 62% of farmers collected no subsidy at all. This way of doing business clearly benefits large farms while small farms are losing out.

Our country's soil is losing its richness and versatility with the prevalence of chemical use and monocropping, which is when a single crop is planted in the same field year after year instead of varying crops across field and season. We're losing our topsoil seventeen times faster than we're

Organic Farming

These days people are learning more and more about how industrialized farming affects our physical health and the health of our planet. Increasingly eaters are voting with their forks and demanding plant and animal products that are certified organic by the U.S. Department of Agriculture (USDA). In 2002, the USDA formalized their national standards for receiving the seal.

USDA Certified Organic means that chemical fertilizers are not part of the farm process, nor are most synthetic herbicides, pesticides, or antibiotics. Animals under this program must be raised on organic feed and have access to the outdoors for at least some of the time. Grazing animals must be allowed to graze. However, there is wiggle room in these requirements: even if only 95% of the ingredients used to feed the animals or to grow the plants are organic, the resulting product can be deemed organic.

For some farmers, food producers, and consumers, being organic is also about a philosophy; they want to use cultivation

and production techniques that emulate nature whenever possible. These farmers work to sustain the health of the earth's soils, ecosystem and people. They rely on ecological processes and on biodiversity, as well as cycles adapted to local conditions.

People wonder why organic products are often more expensive than non-organics. The reason is twofold. First, when you're not relying on chemicals and other non-sustainable methods to grow food, you're not using all the cheap shortcuts that non-organic food producers use. Soil must be enhanced through composting, other non-chemical fertilizers, and crop rotation, but this takes longer which adds to labor expenses. And certain natural cycles,

weather, and disease will impact crops more profoundly, making output less predictable.

Second, while the federal government has slightly increased its support for organic farming over the last several years, offering a small number of food producers incentives and subsidies to use organic methods, the majority of agricultural subsidies still go to large farms that do not use sustainable farming methods. The big dairy, corn, and meat lobbies are not sending their representatives to Washington, DC to gain financial support for organic farmers. The USDA budget for supporting organic farming is miniscule—only a few million dollars a year. All in all, less than 1% of the world's farmland today is devoted to organic farming. Goods produced organically are still relatively scarce, and therefore precious from a price standpoint. To increase the supply of organic foods, we have to use our dollars and our voices to keep the pressure on our elected officials, our food producers, and our food retailers.

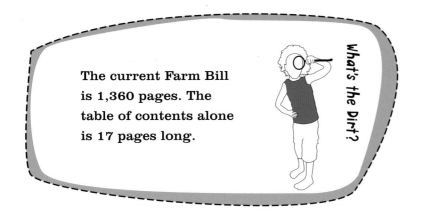

The current Farm Bill is 1,360 pages. The table of contents alone is 17 pages long.

What's the Dirt?

replacing it, we're losing farmers too. In 1950, about 16% of the U.S. population were farmers, but today less than 1%—somewhere between 400,000 and two million people—are farmers. This results in a limited amount of good, fresh food available locally.

The Challenges of Small Farming

Around the time Sadie and Safiyah met Lizbeth, the Angel family was struggling financially, as most small farmers around the country do. When farmers don't use pesticides and chemicals to control bugs and diseases, it can take more people power to protect the crops. Despite the extra work, the Angels want their farm to produce food that's clean and healthy for their community and want to protect themselves from pesticide poisoning when working in the fields. (See sidebar on Organic Farming on page 54.)

In recent years, people have developed a newfound

appreciation for what has been lost as small farms have dwindled. As a result, family-owned and other small farms—many using environmentally sustainable farming practices—are slowly but steadily on the rise. That is good news. The New Farmer Development Project that has supported the Angel Family is part of a larger effort by nonprofit and government organizations around the country to support the small farming movement. These groups are actively financing, advocating, and organizing to support farmers, while encouraging consumers to shop locally, and learn about the importance of sustainability. (See Selected Resources on page 100 for organizations.)

The Angels have had their share of challenges as they've grown their business and gathered experience. Their farm was yielding plentiful crops even in its first seasons, but still they were tens of thousands of dollars in debt. Without a stable

customer base, there was no guaranteed income from the farm that they could count on. Sometimes produce was left to rot on the vine or drop to the ground because they didn't have the money to pay workers to help pick their ripe and ready vegetables and herbs. At the start of their farm journey, the Angels had to learn what would grow best in the Northeastern climate, confronting the usual weather variables: late frosts or too little rain, and other conditions Ana had never encoutnered on her father's farm in Mexico. The third year of the farm's existence was the most difficult. The family initially put their modest savings into the farm, took out loans, and then had a few disappointing crops. This was particularly disheartening after all the labor and effort the entire family had contributed.

The Angels' Urban Oasis

When Sadie and Safiyah first opened the back door that led to the Angels' backyard garden in Brooklyn, they were amazed by how much could be accomplished in such a small space, with just a few hands working. It was an unexpected oasis of lush vegetation in an otherwise stark, urban setting. A month later, when Sadie and Safiyah first visited the Angels' farmland in upstate NY, they fell in love with it. They got right to work weeding and planting eggplant, carrots, beans and other vegetables, which a couple of months later they got to harvest themselves. They grabbed carrot tops and discovered what was hidden in the ground. Seeing how big and

plentiful carrots could grow was a definite high point. Sadie said, "Planting and harvesting with the Angel family was really fun and really hard and really eye-opening." Safiyah said, "I pictured farming to be so tedious and hard… it's hard, but it's fun. I didn't expect it to be that much fun."

For the next couple months, the two girls thought about ways they could help the Angels expand their business. A light bulb went on: maybe they could start a CSA at their school that would be wholly supplied by the Angel family. In this way, it would also be "School Supported Agriculture." They enlisted

How far from
FARM to TABLE?

Some of the foods we eat are grown close to where we live — in our state, town, or back yards. Other foods travel across the country or the world before they end up on our plates. All that transport uses a lot of energy and fuel. The purpose of this game is to be the player whose food has gone the shortest distance from farm to table.

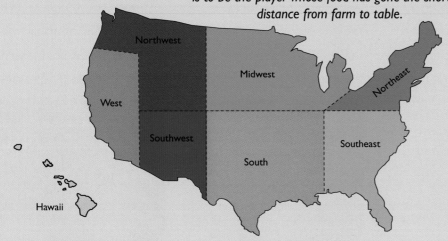

Mileage Calculator ← Where your food comes from →

Your Region ↓	Northwest	Southwest	West	Midwest	South	Northeast	Southeast	Hawaii	Alaska	Mexico	Tanzania	New Zealand	Turkey	Ecuador	China
Northwest	100	1200	1000	2000	2500	3200	2800	3000	2500	2750	11000	7000	6000	4200	5500
Southwest	1300	100	750	1000	1000	1750	1750	2750	4000	1000	10000	6750	6750	3200	6500
West	1000	750	100	2000	2000	3000	2500	2500	3500	1750	10750	6500	6800	3500	6300
Midwest	2000	1000	2000	100	750	1000	1000	4000	4500	1750	8500	8200	5500	3000	6600
South	2500	1000	2000	750	100	1300	750	4000	4500	1250	8500	7500	6000	2500	7250
Northeast	3200	2500	3000	1000	1300	100	1000	5000	4750	2500	7750	9000	5000	3000	6750
Southeast	2800	1750	2500	1000	750	1000	100	4500	4500	1500	7500	8000	5750	2500	7200
Hawaii	3000	2750	2500	4000	4000	5000	4500	100	2750	3750	11000	4500	8000	5500	5100
Alaska	2500	4000	3500	4000	4500	4750	4500	2750	100	5000	7500	7000	5500	5600	4000

HOW TO PLAY

1. Each player picks a region. You can pick: Northwest, Southwest, West, Midwest, South, Northeast, Southeast, Hawaii or Alaska. Only one region per player.

2. Cut up the playing cards on the next page and put them in a pile.

3. When it's your turn, pick a card. Use the Mileage Calculator to figure out approximately how many miles your food has traveled. Record the miles on a score sheet.

4. The game is over when all the cards are used up. The player with the least miles wins!

Playing Cards

Watermelon Southwest	**Bagged Lettuce** West	**Oranges** Southeast	**Cheddar cheese** Midwest	**Chicken** South
Box of Cereal South	**Rhubarb** Northwest	**Peaches** Southeast	**Bananas** Ecuador	**Hamburger** New Zealand
Crab Northeast	**Gala Apple** Northwest	**Butter** small farm in your state 150 miles	**Pineapple** Hawaii	**Blueberries** Northeast
Pink Lady Apple New Zealand	**Asparagus** West	**Garlic** China	**Eggs** small farm in your state 150 miles	**Apple Juice** China
Corn Midwest	**Cocoa** Ecuador	**Salmon** Alaska	**Cashews** Tanzania	**Olive oil** Turkey
Sweet Potatoes South	**Tomatoes** Mexico	**Carrots** local community garden 0 miles	**Coffee** Tanzania	**Strawberries** West
Fresh Lettuce local garden 0 miles	**Yogurt** Midwest	**Beef** Southwest	**Hazelnuts** Turkey	**Avocado** Mexico

they produced more than forty different vegetables in their fields, including several varieties of squash; carrots; corn; radishes; beets; three types of hot chili peppers, including red, green habañero, and banana; Halloween pumpkins; chives; papalo—a salad herb popular in Mexico; mustard greens; beans; and tomatoes.

The Angels spend every possible minute on the farm or sharing their fresh and healthy products that are a direct result of their hard work. Although they don't use pesticides or chemicals of any kind, their farm isn't certified organic because the certification process is very expensive. The Angel family uses sustainable farming techniques to produce food that is fresh and can be distributed locally. When the families in the CSA get their vegetables for the week, they know they are getting healthy, high-quality produce, and that

twenty-eight families to take part. An Angel Family Farm CSA was born! While this certainly didn't solve all of the Angel's financial struggles, it was a step in the right direction. The girls learned how much of a difference they could make by caring, thinking creatively, collaborating with others, learning new skills, and following through.

Wonderful Bounty

When Ana talks about their farm these days, it's with a sense of delighted wonder that she and her family now supply four farmers markets and three CSAs in New York City. With the added secure income from their recent successful season, they were able to purchase a ten-acre parcel of land to farm near their original plot that they continue to lease. Although it's still hard to make a living, things keep looking up. In 2010

A Tale of Two . . .

Most people think that tomato pasta sauce comes from Italy. While it's true that Italian cuisine uses a lot of tomato sauce—the tomato is actually native to South America. It didn't come to Europe until after the Spanish conquest of the Americas. The Italian way of eating pasta and tomato sauce arrived to the United States in the mid 1800s—and quickly became a staple American meal.

Tomato Sauces

Not all tomato sauces are equal!
Take a look at how these two different sauces match up.

Conventional Tomato Sauce

(--) *Typical tomato sauce comes from a jar or a can. It can live in your pantry for years.*

(--) *Salt added! One serving contains 20% of your daily recommended salt intake.*

(--) *Sugar added! 3 teaspoons per serving*

(--) *May contain High Fructose Corn Syrup.*

(--) *Ingredients can come from all over the country, or the world. They are mixed together at a food processing plant, put in jars and shipped out to grocery stores on trucks.*

Fabulous Tomato Sauce

(+) *Make your own tomato sauce! You only need a few ingredients: tomatoes, olive oil, salt, and pepper.*

(+) *You can also add onions, garlic, basil, oregano, olives, eggplant, mushrooms, red pepper, spinach, or zucchini.*

(+) *Homemade sauce is not processed, bottled, shipped or sold. It is only planted, grown, picked and cooked.*

(+) *No sugar, preservatives or unknown ingredients. Packed with veggies and vitamins. Delicious!*

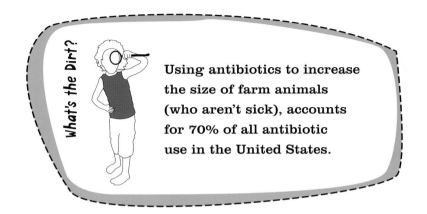

What's the Dirt?

Using antibiotics to increase the size of farm animals (who aren't sick), accounts for 70% of all antibiotic use in the United States.

of caring for crops by hand—are more expensive. Double-check to be sure that all of the vendors there are growers and producers. Don't be shy about asking when something was picked to be sure it's fresh. Bring cash and reusable bags. Most importantly, make friends with the farmers. It makes your food taste better, no kidding.

The stories of the growing bond between the Angel family

it didn't have to travel halfway around the world to make it to their tables. And the Angels enjoy eating what they've grown too. They're looking to purchase a second freezer so they'll be able to eat more of their own food year round.

Farming Grows Community

Every weekend, Lizbeth works with her family selling veggies and herbs and has come up with a few tips for shopping at farmers markets. She recommends going early in the day, when the food is at its freshest and the most robust items are still available. She suggests letting the season guide meal planning and purchases. Buy for value, but appreciate that some foods may be more expensive at the farmers market than on the shelf at the supermarket. Corn, tomatoes, cucumbers, beans, and squash are often cheaper at a farmers market. Many other foods—due to their smaller crop size, the use of more expensive heirloom seeds, and the time and effort

and Sadie and Safiyah and the new relationship between their school and the Angel family CSA are particularly inspiring. Often, what we need to make our lives work is a well-knit community, and the belief that if we don't find what we need, we can make it happen together. Lizbeth says having the farm has changed the way her family sees the world, how they eat together and also who makes up her community. She and her siblings are proud of what they're doing, and they especially like being able to share their expertise as young farmers with their friends and classmates. Like other families in this book, the Angel Family is forging their own path and creating a unique family culture from the values and experiences they share. In the next chapter, we'll greet the newest member of our community, baby Ida, and see how food influences her family's traditions and adventures.

Farm Bill

In 2008 the Food, Conservation and Energy Act was signed into law. This is the latest Farm Bill. Since 1933, this mammoth document has been ratified every five years or so. It impacts the school lunch program and how safe our food is. Since 1965, it has also established which crops qualify for government subsidy. In short, it determines what and how we eat, not only in the US it turns out, but around the world. Many agree that it should be known as the Food Bill so that it would place the interests of eaters first—that is to say: "to promote the quality of our food (and farming) over and above its quantity."

The current bill continues to subsidize the production of high-fructose corn syrup, which makes it harder to fight the

obesity epidemic. And it still favors corporate-owned, big agribusinesses over small farmers, and increases support for the production of cellulosic ethanol.

The bill also has several positive components, like increasing food stamp benefits. It allows public schools to favor local farms in bids for school food, which gives farm-to-school programs a far greater chance to succeed. The bill authorizes more money for land conservation and gives some incentives to farmers to manage their land in ecologically sound ways. It provides funding for local food programs that increase our direct access to healthy food, such as the Farmers Market Promotion Program, Community Food Project Grants and the Healthy Urban Food Enterprise Development Center.

Although overwhelming and complex, the Farm/Food Bill is something we should participate in shaping. Every five years, we must press Congress to make the new version of the bill stronger in its support of farmers and eaters.

Garlic Chicken Soup for Dress-Up

- ✓ 1 whole skinless natural or organic chicken (with or without gizzards—remember to remove them from the body cavity)
- ✓ 7 whole cloves peeled garlic
- ✓ 3 medium zucchini, washed and sliced ½ inch wide
- ✓ 4 medium carrots, chopped into 3-inch pieces
- ✓ 1 liter organic chicken stock (or a low- or no-salt bouillon cube)
- ✓ 1 cup cooked and rinsed brown rice (wild rice works well too!)

THAI INSPIRED: Add ¼ cup coconut milk, 3 slices ginger and the juice of 3 limes to the pot before serving.

LIGHT GREENS: Add baby bok choy, snow peas and scallions to the pot before serving.

SPICY VERSION: Offer cayenne pepper, lemon, avocado, cilantro and parmesan as garnishes.

GRECIAN INSPIRED: Add feta cheese, a sprig of parsley and ½ tablespoon olive oil.

SWEET CRUNCHY SURPRISE: Drop *fresh* corn kernels (yes, uncooked) onto your soup (like miniature fresh croutons)

Play dress up with your soup!

1. Stuff carrot pieces into chest cavity of whole, skinned chicken and place in stock pot with all ingredients except rice. Add water to cover and boil for 1 hour.
2. Test chicken. Once it is done, cook 15 more minutes for super-tender, fall-off-the-bone meat.
3. Remove entire chicken (including carrots and any gizzards or bones) from broth.
4. Let broth cool and carefully hand-mash using masher or large fork, or use a stick blender to liquefy the vegetables and garlic pieces.
5. Add carrots, rice and shredded chicken to broth.
6. Reheat soup over medium heat, allowing the rice to cook for 15 more minutes. If you want more (or thinner) broth, add more chicken stock.

Purslane Potato Salad

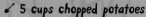

- ✓ 5 cups chopped potatoes
- ✓ ½ to 1 whole cucumber
- ✓ 1 cup purslane leaves and buds
- ✓ 1 cup chopped scallions with greens
- ✓ white vinegar—a splash
- ✓ salt to taste
- ✓ mayonnaise or Nayonnaise mixed with ground chili pepper powder (not flakes)

Some people consider purslane a weed. It can be used to flavor stews, thrown into an omelet/scrambled eggs at the very end of cooking, or eaten raw. It's peppery and lemony, and happens to go nicely with potatoes.
—Gina, Angel Family CSA Blog

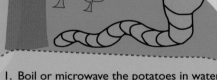

1. Boil or microwave the potatoes in water until edible; drain and set aside to cool.
2. Halve the cucumber, scoop out the seeds and slice into thin crescent moons.
3. Place in a large bowl/container. Add the scallions and purslane leaves.
4. Toss by hand, adding a splash of white or cider vinegar and salt to taste.
5. Add the potatoes and toss again.
6. Mix in several tablespoons of mayonnaise to taste and serve.

Nectarines (or any stone fruit) in Syrup

- ✓ 4-6 nectarines (or any stone fruit)
- ✓ 3 cups water
- ✓ 4 Tbs. sugar

This recipe is so ridiculously easy I hesitate to call it a recipe. As a bonus, you can use bruised fruit and it still tastes good.
—Gina, Angel Family CSA Blog

1. First, halve the fruits to remove the stones.
2. Cut each half into two or three pieces depending on the size of the fruit.
3. Bring water to boil and remove from heat.
4. Pour boiling water over the fruit (I use a colander so the water drains right through).
5. Place the fruit (without water) in a bowl.
6. Toss with sugar until every piece of fruit is covered and set aside.
7. In a little while it will form its own syrup.

Tamales by Angels

Tamale Filling
- ✓ 1 organic rotisserie chicken
- ✓ 1 large onion, chopped
- ✓ 1 clove garlic, sliced
- ✓ 2 Tbs. olive oil
- ✓ 4 dried California chili pods
- ✓ 2 cups water
- ✓ 1½ tsp. salt

¡que delicioso!

Tamale Dough
- ✓ 2 cups masa harina
- ✓ 1 (10½ ounce) can organic chicken broth
- ✓ 1 tsp. baking powder
- ✓ ½ tsp. salt
- ✓ ⅔ cup vegetable shortening
- ✓ 1 (8 ounce) package dried corn husks
- ✓ 1 cup sour cream

1. Use rubber gloves to remove stems and seeds from the chili pods. Place chilis in a saucepan with 2 cups water. Simmer, uncovered, for 20 minutes, then remove from heat to cool.
2. Transfer the chilis and water to a blender and blend until smooth. Strain the mixture, stir in salt, and set aside.
3. Soak the corn husks in a bowl of warm water. In a large bowl, beat the vegetable shortening with a tablespoon of the broth until fluffy. Combine the masa harina, baking powder and salt; stir into the vegetable shortening mixture, adding more broth as necessary to form a spongy dough.
4. In a large sauté pan add chopped onions, garlic and olive oil. Over medium heat cook until just brown and the onions have sweat. Shred the chicken and add meat to pan mix in one cup of the chili sauce. Simmer ingredients over low heat stirring regularly for 4 minutes.
5. Spread the dough out over the corn husks to ¼ to ½ inch thickness. Place one tablespoon of the chicken filling into the center. Fold sides of the husks in toward the center and place in a steamer. Steam for 1 hour.
6. Remove tamales from husks and drizzle remaining chili sauce over. Top with sour cream. For a creamy sauce, mix sour cream into the chili sauce.

Chapter Six

WHAT'S IN YOUR BABY FOOD?

Anna & Ida

Anna Lappé is a second-generation food visionary who has been a mentor to Sadie and Safiyah. She is hands-on, down-to-earth, brilliant, and fun. Sadie and Safiyah took her their questions about food supply, packaging, and the prevalence of high-fructose corn syrup. They especially wanted to know, "Why do people make foods that are bad for us?" Given her regular work as an author and activist, and her new duties as a first-time mother, we were lucky that she found time to sit down and serve up her unique wisdom on the topic of sustainability and food.

Anna's mother, Frances Moore Lappé, started a revolution with the 1971 publication of her book, *Diet for a Small Planet*, which has sold three million copies worldwide. Frances was among the first to expose the enormous waste built into U.S. grain-fed meat production and called for a "plant- and planet–centered" diet. Anna has continued in the family business, writing, informing and provoking. She and her mother co-authored *Hope's Edge* and co-founded the Small Planet Institute, a network for research and popular education about the root causes of hunger. Anna's own book, *Diet for a Hot Planet: The Climate Crisis at the End of Your Fork and What You Can Do About It*, shows how improving our individual health and the health of the planet starts with being more conscious about what we eat. She's also an expert on "greenwashing," when companies use marketing and PR to create the perception that a product or practice is environmentally friendly—when it's not.

Your Baby, Your Food

Anna's family legacy laid the groundwork for a lifetime of good eating habits. She's never been much of a consumer

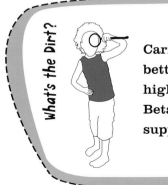

What's the Dirt?

Carrots help you see better at night! They are high in Vitamin A and Beta Carotene, both of which support healthy vision.

of junk food. She's a long-time adherent of a plant-centered diet, and tries to steer clear of processed foods. When she became pregnant, she was extra careful about what she ate since she was also feeding her baby in utero. It was a strong reminder of how hard it is to access chemical-free food on a day-to-day basis. Anna discovered that only .5% of all the farmland in the United States is devoted to organic farming. And only 2.6% of the USDA's agricultural research budget goes to studying organic farming practices. The growing demand for organic food is clearly not being met by the existing supply or government support.

Despite the challenges, Anna felt there was still room for improvement in her diet. Luckily, she and her husband John love to cook. On Sundays, they got into the habit of preparing "a big pot of something," such as organic green lentils with garlic and onions, cannellini and kale soup, or black bean chili. That big pot allows them to count on healthy, prepared food for the rest of the week.

Anna also prefers to drink whole milk and eat yogurt that is made from whole milk. She says, "I believe in whole milk—eating less of the real is better than gorging on the low fat stuff." She adds, "But I am very picky about my dairy, and

seek out producers whose reputations I know and trust. If I've actually been to their farm, that's an added bonus. I know too much about the conditions of most dairy cows on American Concentrated Animal Feeding Operations (CAFOs) to be able to stomach it for my family."

In general, Anna likes to think about little ways to make it easier to eat healthy. For example, often when she buys a bunch of kale, as soon as she gets home she washes it, cuts off the tough stems, and slices it thin. Then, she can easily toss it into her scrambled eggs in the morning or into a stir-fry the following evening. One of her kitchen's secret ingredients is dried porcini mushrooms because they add lots of flavor to many dishes. They're not cheap, but Anna only needs a few added with other, less expensive mushrooms, to extract their delicious punch, so to her they're worth it.

When Anna's daughter Ida Marshall-Lappé was born, Anna decided Ida's first food should be breast milk, so she

nursed her baby, always being careful about what she herself was eating. Anna says, "I definitely believe that if you can nurse, nursing is best, for a host of reasons, from the health benefits to the baby, the health benefits to the mom, to the ease factor, to bonding with the baby. But I also have many friends who for different reasons were unable to breastfeed. Thankfully there are better infant formulas on the market today than when our mother's were raising us." As with milk, there are different types of formula for the various needs of different babies. Whether made from cow's milk or soy, baby formulas today contain adequate iron and there are now organic options. There are even hypoallergenic formulas now available for babies with allergies to both milk and soy. Breast milk or formula is all a baby needs for the first months of life.

When they were ready to introduce Ida to solid foods, Anna and John decided to feed Ida a wide variety. Researching this topic, Anna found that babies are hardwired to be interested in many different foods and flavors, not just bland foods. In fact, Anna says, "I was surprised to discover that, with a few important exceptions, your kid can basically eat

what you eat if you just slightly mash, smoosh or cut it up." She makes her own baby food using a mini food processor, which takes virtually no extra time or special skills. On Ida's plate are some things that might surprise a lot of people, such as black bean stew, eggplant, zucchini, summer squash, and other fruits and vegetables.

There isn't agreement on the ideal first food for babies, and cultural preferences are changing all the time. Back in the 50s, many went along with the advertising. That baby's first food should be Gerber's baby cereal, which is sweet, mild and iron-fortified. Today, pediatricians have more varied recommendations. Many feel that orange veggies, such as squash or sweet potatoes, are best. Vegetables like avocado, with their creamy texture and high nutrient content, are also popular. Anna likes to make her own baby cereal by grinding up grains—such as rice or oatmeal—by using a blender or even a simple mortar and pestle.

Sometimes the healthiest choices for shopping and eating are the most expensive, but this isn't necessarily true when making your own baby food. Families who make their own baby food can save hundreds of dollars a year not buying jarred products. But more importantly, Anna points out, making your own baby food ensures you know exactly what ingredients are going into your baby's body. Processed baby foods often contain trace amounts of chemicals, including pesticides, herbicides and fungicides. Many jarred baby foods contain high fructose corn syrup, tapioca, gelatin, sugar, salt and other additives that not only don't add nutritional value, but also lay the groundwork for poor diets in the future.

Choosing organic foods, or foods raised with few toxic chemicals, is especially important for kids. Landmark research in the early 1990s showed that children and infants are more vulnerable to pesticide residues in their food, in part because pound-for-pound of body weight, children eat and drink more. Plus, they tend to eat more of certain kinds of fruits and vegetables. This became vivid for Anna when Ida started eating solid food. "Ida had a banana love affair! She'd devour them daily. A whole one was about as long as her arm and I pictured what that would mean if I ate that much banana." Plus, Anna reminds us, children's immune systems are less developed and provide less protection than those of an adult—all the more reason to choose real foods without chemicals and additives.

Beyond that, when you make baby food yourself, it's not produced in a factory, and stored in a jar in the first place, so you save on production, transportation and storage energy as well as minimizing what has to be thrown out or recycled later.

Around the Table

Anna and John don't just want to be sure that they are feeding Ida the healthiest possible foods. They want to instill in their daughter a sense of family and community about food and mealtime. To engage her daughter from an early age in the process of preparing meals, Anna loves to put Ida in a sling

How do babies grow?

Babies of all species need energy to grow.

A baby turtle  needs:

Love   Water   Crickets

to turn into

a grown-up turtle

A baby chick needs:

Love   Water   Grains

to turn into

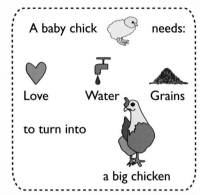

a big chicken

A baby tomato plant needs:

Love   Water   Sun

to turn into

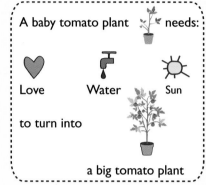

a big tomato plant

A human baby needs:

Love   Water   Bananas

to turn into

a big kid

How did YOU grow so big?

What was the first solid food I ate?

_____

What was my favorite food as a baby?

_____

What food do I eat now that I didn't eat when I was younger?

Sit down with your parents or someone who has known you since you were a baby and answer these questions.

How to Play

1. Grab colored pencils or markers and a die. (You can also use little gadgets if you want to play the game again.)

2. Pick your player. You can be a:

3. When it's your turn, roll the die. Start from one of the 3 boxes in front of your player. Move foward the number of squares you rolled. You can move to the front, side or diagonal—but not backward.

4. Your goal is to make it to the other side to meet up with the grown-up version of your player. The one who makes it there first wins!

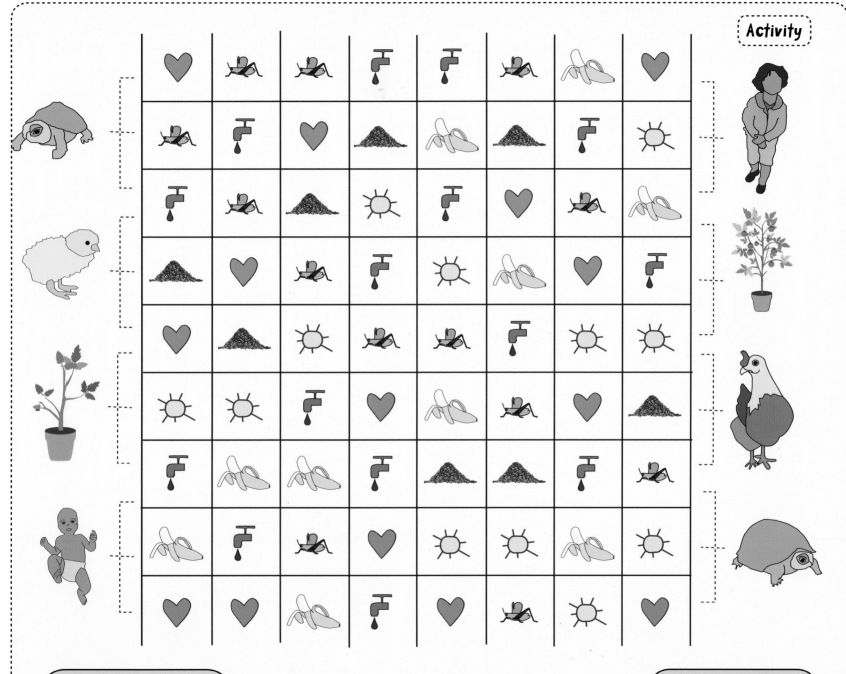

Activity

START... → FINISH!

What's the Dirt?

Popcorn has been around for almost 6,000 years.

to the truth and teaches the rest of us how to separate reality from media spin in the food system. Through her mother, she first learned about the connection between what we eat and the condition of our planet. Now she's a leading expert on this subject. We all look forward to Ida's growth, to seeing how her journey helps her thrive. It's amazing what kids can do when given encouragement and respect. In the next chapter, we meet Oliver, a young farmer from California, who tracked us down in his quest to create a strong, youth-led, in-the-garden community that is not afraid to step forward and speak up.

chair on the kitchen floor, and then sit right down with her. She takes her cutting board and chops and dices while describing to Ida what she's doing. Ida clearly enjoys watching her mom peel oranges, cut into watermelon, and slice avocados. Anna hopes that by showing Ida how food is prepared—by giving her a sense of what real food looks like—she's giving her the best possible foundation for a lifelong, positive relationship to fresh, healthy food.

Instead of using a high chair, Ida's parents attach an infant seat directly to the table, so she's right there with them. Like many new parents, they get together frequently with their extended family, much more than they did before the baby was born. Before digging in, they often take a moment to hold hands and say something about the meal they are about to eat or whatever's on their minds. It is that little moment of pause that Anna particularly loves.

Anna's approach to food is as celebratory and familial as it is politically aware. In her writing and advocacy, she gets

Milk in Schools

Cows milk, soy milk, rice milk, goats milk... the list goes on. Chocolate, vanilla, strawberry, and plain. Raw milk, cream, half and half, whole, reduced fat, low fat, skim. Organic and conventional. Who can make sense of the ever-expanding milk aisle?

One thing is for certain: it's hard to overestimate the power of the milk lobby in our country, which is one of the reasons it is so difficult to figure out for ourselves what the pros and cons are of drinking cow's milk in particular. Beginning in 1954 the Special Milk Program legislation has offered federal reimbursement for each half pint of milk served to children in schools. Schools represent sales of 460 million gallons of milk per year in the U.S., or 7% of total milk sales. In light of the debate over how healthy it really is for our kids and how much they need to drink, the line blurs between whether milk is provided in schools for nutritional

reasons or whether it is a holdover from the old days as a key source of revenue for the dairy manufacturers.

Milk was once the natural product of cows. Cows grazed grass on pastures, and were allowed to produce milk on a seasonal schedule. But today's cow's milk is a different product altogether, and most of it can no longer be called natural. Most dairy cows today are fed grain, not grass, and this grain—usually a mixture of corn, soy and hay—is routinely enhanced with antibiotics. In addition, many cows today are kept

inside and forced to manufacture milk all year round without a break. Because this depletes them and often makes them sick and unproductive, they are fed hormones, additional antibiotics and other supplements to keep them working. So while it's true that cow's milk has some beneficial properties, such as providing calcium and vitamin D, it is not the perfect and indispensable drink it is marketed as and in fact may be a large part of the reason for increased incidences of allergies, ear infections, digestive problems, and even obesity, diabetes, and early menstruation.

Many points can be made from all sides of the Great Milk Debate. The most important thing is that you figure out what works best for yourself and your family given your allergies, tastes, philosophical beliefs, budget, eating habits, food culture, physical needs, and style.

Build-Your-Own Burritos

- ✓ 1 cup diced white or red onions
- ✓ 2 bell peppers (yellow, red or green)
- ✓ 2 cups sliced mushrooms
- ✓ 2 cups cooked rice
- ✓ 10 tortillas

Optional Ingredients
- ✓ grated cheese
- ✓ shredded cooked chicken
- ✓ your favorite salsa
- ✓ shredded carrots
- ✓ shredded or chopped lettuce
- ✓ chopped cilantro
- ✓ fresh chopped mangoes
- ✓ sour cream (thinned with a little nonfat milk)

Picky eaters unite! With this meal you can be as choosy as you want. Pick your ingredients, wrap 'em up, and enjoy.

1. In medium pan, sauté onions, pepper, and mushrooms until combined and fragrant. Place in serving bowl with spoon.
2. Toast tortillas in a dry pan until lightly browned. Put in tray wrapped in cloth napkin or bandana.
3. Add assorted optional ingredients to separate bowls and place on table.
4. Call friends and family to table and invite them to assemble their own burrito!

Coconut Peach Ice Cream

- ✓ 3 cups coconut milk
- ✓ 2 cups diced fresh peaches
- ✓ 6 Tbs. agave nectar
- ✓ ⅛ tsp. fine sea salt
- ✓ 2 Tbs. arrowroot powder

Nothing says summer like peaches and coconuts. Try this ice cream when it's hot and muggy out. Or put on some surf tunes and serve it at a summer party in the middle of winter. Either way, it's yum!

1. In a small cup, mix ¼ cup of the coconut milk with the arrowroot to make a slurry. In a medium saucepan over medium heat, combine the remaining coconut milk, agave nectar, and salt with the coconut milk slurry. Warm until starting to thicken, 2–3 minutes.
2. Transfer to the refrigerator until completely cold.
3. Pour cold mixture into an ice cream maker and freeze until creamy, 25–30 minutes. Add the peaches during the last minute of freezing. Transfer to an airtight container and place in a freezer until firm, about 2 hours.

Sweet Potato-licious

Inspired by a recipe from Marion Bell, Metropolitan Hospital Center, in *Go Green East Harlem*, edited by Manhattan Borough President Scott Stringer

- ✓ 3 sweet potatoes
- ✓ 3 large eggs, whites separated and yolks discarded
- ✓ ¼ cup condensed milk
- ✓ ¼ cup honey
- ✓ ¾ Tbs. pure vanilla extract
- ✓ ¼ Tbs. ground cinnamon
- ✓ ⅛ Tbs. ground nutmeg
- ✓ 7 oz. chunky pineapple in juices
- ✓ ½ cup sugar
- ✓ ½ cup cinnamon applesauce
- ✓ ¼ cup raisins
- ✓ ¼ cup shredded coconut

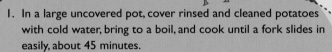

1. In a large uncovered pot, cover rinsed and cleaned potatoes with cold water, bring to a boil, and cook until a fork slides in easily, about 45 minutes.
2. Drain and let cool until you can comfortably handle them. Gently pinching the tips of the potatoes, slip and slide off the skin, discard. Place remaining potatoes in a large mixing bowl. Mash until smooth, discarding any stringy pieces.
3. Add ¼ cup of the egg whites (reserving the rest), all the other liquid ingredients, and the powdered spices. Mix thoroughly. Add fruit and its juice, raisins, and coconut. Mix with a spatula.
4. Using an electric blender set at high, mix the reserved egg whites until they turn white, fluffy, and stiff.
5. Pour potato mixture into 9×9-inch casserole dish, lightly greased with oil. Using a spatula, fold and turn the beaten egg whites on top of the potato mixture but do not mix or blend. (Over-mixing will stop the egg whites from rising in the oven.)
6. Bake alone in the oven at 350°F for 45–50 minutes. Let cool and serve warm, as a side dish or for dessert.
7. Delicious!

Pesto Sandwiches

Pesto
- ✓ 4 garlic cloves
- ✓ ¾ cup pine nuts (¼ pound)
- ✓ 2 cups grated Parmigiano-Reggiano
- ✓ 2 cups grated Pecorino Romano
- ✓ 5 cups basil leaves
- ✓ 2 cups packed flat-leaf parsley leaves
- ✓ 5 Tbs. olive oil
- ✓ salt and pepper

Sandwich
- ✓ 2 baguettes
- ✓ 2 whole tomatoes
- ✓ 2 lbs. fresh mozzarella

Kofi is really good at making these for the whole family!

1. Chop garlic in the food processor.
2. Add nuts, parmigiano and pecorino cheeses, salt and pepper and half of the herbs.
3. Blend until all your ingredients are chopped.
4. Add the rest of the herbs, one handful at a time.
5. When everything is chopped, add the oil and blend until incorporated. Your pesto is ready!
6. Slice the tomatoes and mozzarella cheese.
7. Cut the baguettes in sections and then length-wise, so they look like an open face sandwich.
8. Spread a thick layer of pesto on the baguettes. Add tomato and mozzarella. Put in the toaster or regular oven for 4 minutes to toast.

Chapter Seven

WHO'S OLIVER?

Derek, Sophie, Marcia, Oliver and Tess

Nothing better epitomizes the ripple effect communities have on one another than what happened when a twelve-year-old boy named Oliver Taylor met a man named Siamack Sioshansi. Siamack was helping to launch an urban gardening initiative called Urban Farmers in Oliver's hometown of Lafayette, California, where Oliver and his two older sisters, Sophie and Tess, live with their parents, Marcia and Derek.

The Urban Farmers

Siamack met with Oliver's mom to talk about a pilot program cultivating sustainable environments in metropolitan and urban areas. The organization wanted to partner with twenty families in the area who had available plots of land of 300

square feet or more. The Taylors qualified. If they supplied the land and water, the Urban Farmers would provide the labor and expertise. The family would get to help cultivate their yard as productive farmland and would receive all the food they could eat from their crop yields. Any remaining food would be distributed to neighbors and local charities. Marcia was all for it.

Oliver was at home that morning sitting at the table, learning from Siamack about fruit tree varieties, air quality, and the abundance of sweet, yummy snacks that he might be able to pick himself. Like Marcia, he knew right away that he wanted to be involved. Through the Urban Farmer's program, Siamack became Oliver's gardening mentor and suggested that his first steps should be learning and researching. Oliver began devouring books on food and food politics. He scoured the web for as much information as he could find. He invited

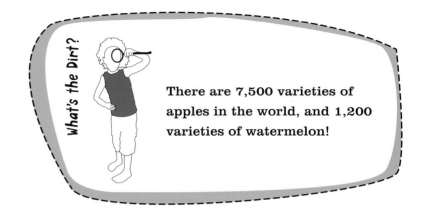

friends to join in the backyard fruit tree planting party. He enlisted his mom to help him do more research. She discovered our website and read our blog and told Oliver about the **What's On YOUR Plate?** project. Soon he was our biggest fan. Then we became his.

As Oliver tended the backyard orchard and garden, he continued to learn about the issues surrounding food and sustainability. He read about Alice Waters, the legendary chef and food activist who founded Chez Panisse, an early local food restaurant in Northern California. He found out that her Edible Schoolyard project which promotes gardening and eating fresh food in schools happens to be only 15 miles from his home.

Alice's idea had been to take a one-acre plot of land, and as part of the Martin Luther King, Jr. Middle School curriculum, to work with the school's students, teachers, and gardening staff, teaching kids how to grow and prepare food. In this way, students learn firsthand about the connection

What's a Face Space?

You can't grow food with a computer. But the Internet can help you grow your community. Websites, blogs, and social networking sites like Facebook, Twitter, YouTube, and Flickr can bring together kids, parents, teachers, families, friends, and complete strangers, outside of school hours and despite our conflicting schedules. The Internet is a dynamic part of our social environment and often helps us talk to each other about what's important in our lives.

While kids get more and more comfortable on these sites, parents struggle to understand how they work. Parents worry about how the Internet puts kids in danger, but kids enjoy the Web's potential to empower them to succeed in society. Kids adapt to new technologies more quickly than adults. My daughter Sadie still has to program my smartphone for me—just like I still teach my mother how to use the settings on her digital camera.

In this chapter, Oliver Taylor instinctively knew Facebook could connect him to a bigger world of food justice. He might have been too young to buy a ten-acre farm or start a farmers' market, but the food reform community was there online, ready to embrace, support and educate him, and ready to be enriched by him in turn. He not only worked to improve his neighborhood but he also contributed to a national movement. This is the power of online communities.

We can network with each other in hundreds of ways in a matter of hours. We can do fun things like look up new recipes for old favorites. We can find and share solutions to common garden pest problems. We can educate ourselves with online games or informational websites. We can connect with others who share our vision of making ourselves, and our planet, healthier. Online together, we can advocate for local, regional and national policy change. The food is still in the dirt, but farmers are online.

between everyday food choices and their health, as well as the health of the community and the environment. They learned to appreciate food as "a means of awakening the senses, encouraging awareness of the transformative values of nourishment, community, and stewardship of the land." It's a perfect example of how something simple like a garden can educate, feed, and grow community. Alice was way ahead of the curve when she founded it in 1995. These days, the Edible Schoolyard has become a gold standard, with similar efforts on large and small scales happening nationwide. You can find school gardens in every state from Louisiana to Ohio. Oliver found out that there are more than 4,000 in California alone.

Activist in Training

Siamack, now a close friend, told Oliver about a Disney grant for $500 called Friends for Change. Oliver looked it over and decided to apply. His goal? To cover expenses for a screening of **What's On YOUR Plate?** at his school. In the weeks leading up to the due date for the grant application, he started a Facebook page about the Urban Farmers' efforts, enlisting classmates, friends and family to help. He set a challenge for himself: he

would bring this campaign to the attention of at least 500 people on Facebook before the day the grant application was due. He would show Disney, through his enthusiasm and initiative, why he deserved to win. Meanwhile, he tended and watered the veggies and fruit tree seedlings sprouting in his family's backyard farm.

Oliver's sisters Tess and Sophie have a lot of friends and are social networkers. They offered to help him build out his Facebook page, by inviting their friends to become fans of "Oliver for the Urban Farmers." His base grew slowly at first but within a couple of weeks it began to go crazy. There were college kids from Atlanta. High school students in Hawaii signed up. Even people in other countries joined in. Meanwhile, we got an email telling us about his page and his efforts to raise money for a **Whats On YOUR Plate?** film screening, so we enlisted our online community to help. Within three weeks—by the time the application was due—he had over eight hundred fans. Perhaps the only person who was surprised on the day Disney announced his grant was Oliver.

Oliver was a quick study for someone so new to affecting

YOU CAN COMPOST

Compost is made by worms and other organisms. Making good compost means keeping your worms healthy and happy.

Do you know what things you should and shouldn't put in your compost pile?

WORM FIND

Make a colony of worms by circling words from the word list.

If you CAN find the words, then these are things that your worms will love and you can put them in your compost pile.

If you CAN'T find the words, then these are materials you should keep out of your compost pile.

apple cores	fur	plastic bags
banana peels	grass clippings	potato skins
beef	hair	rubber bands
cheese	leaves	sawdust
chicken	leftovers	stale bread
coffee filters	moldy veggies	tea bags
coffee grounds	olive pits	tin foil
corn cob	paper bags	toothpicks
dirt	peach pits	vegetable scraps
dog poo	peanut shells	water
dust bunnies	pine needles	weeds
egg shells	pizza boxes	wood chips

S	O	H	A	N	W	J	L	Q	C	G	N	W	L	F	S	B	R	S
O	S	F	N	P	E	A	N	U	T	S	H	E	L	L	S	E	R	O
H	M	F	A	O	R	N	T	S	P	M	T	E	A	B	A	G	S	P
C	O	R	N	C	O	B	S	E	G	O	S	D	N	R	T	G	A	W
S	L	I	B	O	N	D	A	O	R	L	P	S	A	E	R	S	T	O
T	D	M	L	F	A	P	P	E	A	C	H	P	I	T	S	H	P	O
A	Y	D	E	F	T	O	I	N	S	T	A	L	E	B	R	E	A	D
H	V	S	A	E	T	T	Z	D	S	S	I	O	L	A	B	L	P	C
L	E	T	V	E	S	A	Z	O	C	A	R	K	T	N	A	L	E	H
O	G	V	E	G	E	T	A	B	L	E	S	C	R	A	P	S	R	I
R	G	A	S	R	T	O	B	C	I	N	L	O	P	N	T	R	B	P
W	I	O	C	O	N	S	O	M	P	T	F	F	D	A	G	T	A	S
L	E	L	S	U	D	K	X	C	P	H	L	F	M	P	A	O	G	E
T	S	I	A	N	S	I	E	T	I	R	G	E	N	E	T	O	S	G
E	A	V	G	D	M	N	S	F	N	N	S	E	T	E	Y	T	P	L
R	G	E	B	S	S	S	K	L	G	P	A	F	H	L	C	H	Y	U
U	I	P	D	F	G	S	M	L	S	P	W	I	Y	S	D	P	S	T
S	F	I	B	P	I	N	E	N	E	E	D	L	E	S	O	I	A	S
F	R	T	B	T	F	E	R	F	L	N	U	T	T	P	A	C	R	E
D	U	S	T	B	U	N	N	I	E	S	S	E	N	F	A	K	M	T
T	I	W	C	L	R	K	T	U	J	I	T	R	A	N	D	S	G	O
O	N	O	A	P	P	L	E	C	O	R	E	S	M	O	T	E	R	E

TRASH OR TREASURE?

Decide whether you should put the things below in the trash, compost, or recyling, or whether they could be reused.
Draw a line connecting them to your choice. If you think it could be more than one, draw more than one line!

Cardboard Boxes

Milk Jug

Newspaper

Styrofoam

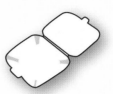

Plastic Bags

Yogurt Containers

Paper Towel Rolls

draw your connecting lines here

RECYCLE

COMPOST

REUSE

LANDFILL

ANSWERS

Cardboard Boxes -- Recycle, Compost or Reuse
Use cardboard boxes to make a fort or spaceship, or as a surface for art projects. You can also recycle cardboard and compost it -- just make sure to soak it with water first.

Paper Towel Rolls -- Recycle, Compost or Reuse
Paper towel rolls are made of cardboard, so they can be recycled. If you put them in your compost pile, soak them in water first. They can also be reused -- for an art project, as a toy for a small pet, or as a make-believe telescope.

Newspapers -- Recyle, Compost or Reuse
Newspapers can be used as wrapping paper, as bedding for your pet, for art projects, or as mulch in the garden. You can also add it to your compost pile or recycle it.

Styrofoam -- Reuse or Landfill
Styrofoam creates a lot of waste. Since it can't be recycled, most ends up in landfills. The best thing to do with styrofoam is to avoid it!

Milk Jug -- Recycle or Reuse
Use old plastic milk jugs to cover the plants in your garden or make them into a bird feeder. You can also recycle milk jugs.

Yogurt Container -- Recycle or Reuse
Most single-size yogurt containers are made of number 5 plastic, which many recycling centers don't accept. Check with your local recycling center. You can use yogurt container in craft projects -- to hold paint, water, beads, or glue.

Plastic Bags -- Reuse or Landfill
You can use plastic bags to pick up dog poo or as trash bags in your home. Many grocery stores also have boxes where you can drop off your plastic bags. But since they can't be recycled, lots of plastic bags end up in landfills. That's why lots of people bring their own cloth bags to the grocery store.

social change. It didn't take long for him to become a genuine spokesman for the urban farm movement, campaigning at school, around town, and in media interviews, locally and beyond. Oliver is not only a natural farmer and chef; he is also a super-talented promoter. He used his grant money to organize screenings at both his school and local library. He spread the word about these events and rallied volunteers as well as partner organizations to co-present with the Urban Farmers.

The Full Cycle

Oliver's mom Marcia was learning alongside her son and felt that she could also make personal changes that would bring her actions in line with her beliefs. She decided to become a vegan, something she always thought would be a tough thing to accomplish. She and her family had taken on the urban farm initiative for environmental reasons and for the food, and to participate in a community project together. But as she got more deeply into the issues surrounding food, she realized

more and more what was at stake. She wanted to try harder to be healthy, to set an example for her children and others, and to minimize her own negative impact on the planet.

The rest of the family hasn't yet followed suit, but they've all gotten a lot more conscious of what they eat, and they spend more time these days convening around the table for meals. Oliver has grown to enjoy cooking meals side by side with his dad. They share something else too: while Marcia has discovered how many varieties of beans there are and how many delicious ways they can be prepared, Oliver and his dad still agree: they don't like beans, period.

Oliver's family enjoys getting creative with salads. With all of the vegetables and fruits they now have growing in their backyard—even an almond tree—there is a lot to choose from. There are almonds, apples, oranges, strawberries, cilantro, peppers, corn, eggplant, lettuces, tomatoes, radishes, and fingerling potatoes. (See recipe on page 88.) Marcia tells us that the birds are still getting to the strawberries first, but she appreciates that: she's excited that the food they're growing supports an ecosystem.

Oliver is discovering that growing his own food and

buying from farmers markets creates a lot of advantages—not just for the birds who get to eat juicy strawberries right off the bush. He found that when he eats food that comes fresh and without a lot of packaging, the amount of garbage and recycling he generates is very small. When you reach into bowls of fruits and vegetables for your meals, you aren't taking microwave-ready dinners out of the freezer and unpacking them. There isn't all that Styrofoam, cardboard and plastic to get rid of. When you shop thoughtfully, buying sustainably grown meat, poultry and fish, and locally grown

produce and dairy, it helps you be more careful about meal planning, and be sure nothing's going to waste.

Oliver uses leftovers in soup, smoothies and salads. But he wants to finish the full cycle. When he and Sadie met in California, he said that after eating, freezing extras, and making leftovers into lunch, he still needs someplace to put the rinds, the cuttings and the cores. So Sadie told him about composting. Lots of people think composting is too hard to do, especially if you live in an apartment, but Sadie assured him that he can figure it out and it's fun. When we started our bin, Sadie hated battling the fruit flies that appeared (they don't appear in everyone's!). But it's important to be patient because compost doesn't happen overnight and can take a few months to establish. Now Sadie revels in the fact that, contrary to popular assumption, the bin doesn't smell bad; in fact, it smells like fresh dirt. It's warm and rich in nutrients for your plants. Since she's been composting, it's become awkward to throw compostable food in a regular trash bin. She's developed a reflex of looking for the compost bin.

Although Oliver will be able to keep his compost outside near the fruit trees, Sadie's is inside our apartment, sitting on a crate in the corner of the kitchen. We add all kinds of kitchen scraps, from tea bags and apple cores to over-ripe fruits and corn husks. Very little edible matter has to go into the landfill outside of meat, dairy, onions, and garlic. (See activity on page 81.) When Sadie opens it to add something, she gets a whiff of the countryside. She likes how hot the air feels on her hands inside the compost bin, which never ceases to amaze her. We have Mother Nature, right here in our kitchen. Her brothers put up colorful signs on our composter, the recy-

cling bins and trash cans. The trash is labeled "landfill" in bold letters.

When the compost is ready, we use it in our window boxes or in the plants that live inside the apartment as an extra boost to their roots. We also mix the liquid that comes from the spout at the side of our compost bin with water and feed that to the plants. None of it goes to waste.

Reduce, Reuse, Recycle

When you commit to recycling, you find that you end up buying a lot less of the stuff you can't reuse, like plastic wrap. When you're vigilant about using up all the leftovers you store in glass containers in your fridge, putting what you can't use into the compost, and buying fewer items such as bottled water, you find that you end up creating a whole ecosystem of your own, one where everything has a place and use.

That's what Oliver's family is doing with their back-yard garden project. They're taking what they have and using it productively to feed themselves and others. By growing more, they can buy less, put nutrients back into the soil and set an example. By doing what they are doing, they are fostering the kind of community that **What's On YOUR Plate?** is all about. Sadie and Safiyah say they wish they could live like bees: "They make their food; they share their food; nothing is wasted; and they get what they need. It just works." A long

time ago, we were more direct participants in our collective ecosystem, but too much of the world developed in such a way that it appears we've lost our place. In both incremental and exponential ways, people like Oliver, Sadie, Caleb, Safiyah, Gabriel, and Lizbeth are creating *their* place in the world and thus impacting the *whole* world.

If it has a seed inside, then it's a fruit, which means peppers, tomatoes and avocados are all fruits.

What's the Dirt?

Smashed Cauliflower

- ✓ 1 head cauliflower
- ✓ 5 cloves fresh garlic
- ✓ water to cover
- ✓ sea salt (to taste)
- ✓ white pepper (to taste)
- ✓ 5 Tbs. extra virgin olive oil

Cauliflowers come in
a variety of colors.
Try the purple ones;
they're so festive on the plate!

1. Prepare cauliflower: rinse head and cut off stem base. Remove all leaves, separate cauliflower florets, drop into large soup pot.
2. Prepare garlic: remove skins and toss whole into pot.
3. Fill the pot with filtered water covering the cauliflower/garlic by 1 inch.
4. Heat on high until boiling. Skim. Lower heat to simmer for 30–45 minutes.
5. Remove from heat and carefully mash all ingredients with a masher or in a blender. Add olive oil, salt and white pepper to taste.

OPTIONAL: Toss in a few sprigs of your favorite fresh herb examples: rosemary, dill, oregano.

SPICY OPTION: Try a few drops of hot sauce and lemon juice in the bowl.

Sophie's Oatmeal Cookies

- ✓ 1½ cups whole oats
- ✓ 1 cup all-purpose flour
- ✓ 1 tsp. baking soda
- ✓ 1 tsp. salt
- ✓ 1 cup (2 sticks) butter, softened
- ✓ ¾ cup granulated sugar
- ✓ ¾ cup packed brown sugar
- ✓ 1 tsp. vanilla extract
- ✓ 2 large eggs
- ✓ 2 cups raisins or dried cranberries
- ✓ 1 cup optional ingredient, like chopped nuts or dried fruits

Oliver's sister Sophie made these
when we visited.
We couldn't get enough!

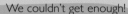

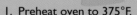

1. Preheat oven to 375°F.
2. Combine flour, oats, baking soda and salt in small bowl.
3. Beat butter, granulated sugar, brown sugar and vanilla extract in large mixer bowl until creamy. Add eggs, one at a time, beating well after each addition. Gradually beat in flour/oat mixture.
4. Stir in raisins and/or other optional ingredients. Drop by rounded tablespoon onto ungreased baking sheets.
5. Bake for 9 to 11 minutes or until golden brown. Cool and share.

Baked Fingerling Potatoes

Recipe

- ✓ 1 lb. fingerling potatoes (any color)
- ✓ 1 cup of your favorite olive oil
- ✓ salt and fresh pepper (to taste)
- ✓ 2 sprigs rosemary
- ✓ 2 tsp. garlic powder
- ✓ 2 tsp. onion powder
- ✓ 3 tsp. Italian seasoning
- ✓ 2 tsp. smoked paprika

Some varieties of fingerling potatoes are called "Russian Banana," "Butterfinger," and "Purple Peruvian."

1. In a large pot filled with water, put all your potatoes and let soak for as long as possible (at least 2 hours). You may even consider buying your potatoes a day early so you can soak them overnight—this allows the starch that gathers during storage to be released into the water. Toss starchy water.
2. Preheat oven to 400°F and prepare a baking sheet with parchment paper or foil.
3. Cut all the potatoes in half and put them in a medium bowl. Add the olive oil first and mix it around so you cover all the potatoes.
4. Add salt and pepper, and mix. Continue down ingredient list, mixing after each one.
5. Spread the potatoes evenly on the baking sheet and put in the oven.
6. Cook for 30–45 minutes. They are done when the skin of the potatoes starts to prune and they are fork tender.
7. Take them out and adding a little more salt and pepper to taste.

Kale Avocado Salad

Recipe

- ✓ ½ cup fresh orange juice
- ✓ 3 Tbs. fresh lemon juice
- ✓ 2 tsp. soy sauce
- ✓ 1 clove garlic, smashed and chopped into a paste
- ✓ 4 Tbs. extra-virgin olive oil
- ✓ 2 avocados, halved, pitted and peeled
- ✓ 2 Tbs. raw hemp seeds (optional)
- ✓ 1 bunch kale (about ¾ lb.), stemmed and finely chopped
- ✓ Kosher salt and freshly ground black pepper, to taste

Did you know there is a kind of kale that is named after dinosaurs? Dino kale has a rough, bumpy exterior, that reminds us of prehistoric reptiles.

1. Whisk together juices, soy sauce and garlic in a bowl. Slowly whisk in oil; set dressing aside.
2. Cut the avocados into ½-inch cubes.
3. Put cubed avocados, half of the hemp seeds, and kale into a serving bowl.
4. Toss kale mixture with dressing and season generously with salt and pepper.

Epilogue

WHO'S COMING TO DINNER?

Tenzin & butterfly

When Sadie and her brothers and I think about food, we think about being together with friends and family, about the tastes and colors on our plates and honoring and celebrating that we are fortunate to have food to eat. When we're sitting down and sharing a meal, we're not only savoring the food, but also reconnecting with everyone around the table.

Our Garden, Ourselves

During the growing season, our small garden thrives in the window boxes that overlook noisy traffic on the street below. Despite living in a crowded, concrete city, Sadie's brother Tenzin and the rest of us benefit from experiencing nature in a meaningful and thoughtful way, and our window gardens plays a big role in helping us achieve that. It has also helped us connect planting and growing with what we bring to the table to eat. As a result, our meals together have become much more fun and rewarding in unexpected ways. Recently, Tenzin was walking home from his school musical performance carrying flowers he'd been given to mark the event. Hugging the bouquet to his chest, he joyfully exclaimed: "I am a garden!"

It's true. Tenzin does have a lot in common with a garden. Looking at him makes us smile. He is full of life and sunshine and the desire to share. He also has an eye for the colorful, the playful, and the decorative. When he's at home and notices that fresh flowers appeared in a vase or that a brightly beaded necklace lies near the bathroom sink, he will often ask: "Is that just for pretty?" When he adds one of his own flourishes to the dinner table—petals delicately strewn about or paper flowers, for example—he'll let me know: "That's just for pretty."

One evening Tenzin asked me to cut up watermelon so

he could put it on the table "just because it's pink." Thinking of food as beautifying the table—satisfying our senses beyond taste—can change what we eat. At that dinner, we discovered that watermelon goes well with burritos. We've also found that the more hands celebrating, the more satisfying it is. Celebration is the motivation and food is the engine.

Community Is a Garden

Like a garden, community is a dynamic process. We had no idea where the **What's On YOUR Plate?** project would take us when we started it. Our community grew around us. We nurtured, watered and harvested it, and it sustains us in return. Working together on the project, we forged something new, a stronger, more confident, and effective group. We worked to slow the epidemics of heart disease, diabetes, and childhood obesity, to support small farmers and save small farms,

CELEBRATE!

Host a festive dinner for family and friends

Recipe Sleuth

Do you have a grandparent, aunt, uncle friend, or neighbor who is a GREAT COOK? Ask them for a favorite recipe that uses local, fresh ingredients and write it down here.

RECIPE:

FROM:

INGREDIENTS:

DIRECTIONS:

recipe sleuth
plan the menu
draw your dinner
set the table

Plan the Menu

What do you plan to eat at this fabulous dinner? Write down the menu here.

The Menu

To Drink:

Starter:

Main Dish:

For Dessert:

Draw Your Dinner

What are you eating tonight?
Draw your food on the plate to your right.

Set the Table

One of the best parts of being the host is setting the table. You can decide where everyone sits and how to decorate the table.

Look at the suggestions below. Which things would you like on your table? Where will your guests sit?

Draw your table, using these pictures as ideas. Make sure to give everyone a name tag.

to ease the destruction of our natural world. We won't accept the landscape of overmedicated, overfed and undernourished, under-nurtured young people. Or the vast swath of bankrupted farmers. Or the fog of a sick planet. Together we are making change. Our work is bigger than we are, and although the view is daunting, we are determined to persevere.

Creating community is one of the most important tasks we can undertake. In the common area of our home, there's a poster on the wall that's entitled, "How to Create Community." These are some of the suggestions: "Plant flowers; look up when you're walking; use your library; buy from local merchants; help a lost dog; take children to the park; fix it even if you didn't break it; pick up litter; talk to the mail carrier; listen to the birds; put up a swing; start a tradition; help carry something heavy; honor elders; bake extra and share; ask for help when you need it; turn up the music; turn down the music; know that no one is silent although many are not heard, work to change this." A few I would add are: paint a mural; create sculptures for a community garden; start a festival or block party; lead an architecture tour through your neighborhood; project a film outdoors; talk to a stranger about an artwork or what he had for breakfast.

Getting Together

Our last scene in the **What's On YOUR Plate?** film is Sadie and Safiyah cooking with eco-chef and author, Bryant Terry, as well as Caleb and other friends. One by one, characters from other scenes in the film arrive with their own homemade dishes, to enjoy the meal and to celebrate the completion of the film and what everyone has learned. Caleb's father John and brother Jojo show up to sample Caleb's sautéed corn. Rachel, Tony and Kofa come to taste Safiyah's caprese salad. Anna Lappé, Kevin Walter from the Stanton Street CSA, and Maritza Owens from Harvest Home mingle in the crowd.

Tenzin made the pasta sauce on our table that evening with tomatoes and basil grown in the window garden. The Angel family arrives later on, having just driven down from their farm upstate. Lizbeth Angel brings tamales she and her

Tenzin's Top Ten Tablesetting Ideas

We never know what Tenzin has in store for the table and setting it up is clearly a joyful task for him. In fact, he has made it his signature, a chance to express himself and to contribute to the family's work at the same time.

* Put flowers on the table. They can be real or made of paper, with blossoms or just the greens, or simply sprinkled petals or leaves. Sometimes the whole flower in bouquets in vases, sometimes individual vases. Think the water glass. Or individually lay a single stem across each plate.

* Put cloth napkins out for everyone. Use bandanas or other swatches of fabric. Fold them, twist them, roll them, or lay them underneath the plates like placemats. Nestled at each seat, they're for use if necessary or "just for pretty."

* The block area doesn't only belong in the kindergarten classroom. Bring the dishes to the table and stack, pile and balance the plates, cups and silverware into a towering dinner table sculpture. Drape a flower across the top.

* Put a water jug on the table and only put ice in everyone's water glass. When people pour the water over the ice, it makes a delicate sound and reflects colors around the table.

* Draw a name tag for each person, not necessarily folded like the tent ones at events, but just a scrap from the recycling bin, written on, decorated, placed on the plate, under the forks, or taped to the back of the chair.

* Use small, unmatched ceramic dishes for all your sauces and side dishes. Never put anything on the table in plastic or packaging or on plain plates. Wrap drawings around glasses, jars and bowls to spruce them up.

* Create a throne for a dinner guest (or a random family member) by tying ribbons on her chair, adorning it with scarves, weaving necklaces through the slats in the back, and providing a special comfy pillow for her to sit on.

* Make sure there are a couple extra, empty dishes and bowls for olive pits, edamame shells, artichoke leaves, and corncobs. (Afterwards, you can throw that stuff in your compost bin, except hold the pits.)

* Choose silverware placement according to design and without a nod toward traditional table setting. The fork can be in an empty glass, at the top or either side of the plate, or on the plate already… knives and spoons only when necessary.

* Pick herbs from the window gardens and dress the edges of the setting with a variety of tastes, smells and textures. Have a choice of cilantro, sage, thyme, or basil to mix in with your meal, to rub between your fingers and smell, or "just for pretty."

mom made with corn, onions and garlic they grew. All farmers, whether they're young, new farmers like Oliver or urban family farmers like the Angels, know that having a hand in getting food to the table adds another dimension to eating. The food is life-sustaining, not life-threatening. People are hopeful and happy. Getting together to grow, cook, share, and celebrate meals puts soul into our food.

Our Journey

We began this book exploring what Sadie and her brothers actually eat. It's hard sometimes to see beyond advertising, but being more aware is a first step towards changing, towards *not* doing something out of habit, convenience or because everyone else is doing it. After examining the cupboards and refrigerator in our kitchen, we went outside to explore the neighborhood and take a closer look at how access to good food can seriously impact your health. Caleb showed us that you have to work hard when seeking out the best food options for the sake of your whole family. Safiyah helped us explore school lunches in order to better understand what they're made of and why, so that we can all work towards improving them. With Gabriel, we learned about how food can impact us physically and emotionally. He and his mother demonstrated how to craft a diet that satisfies his medical requirements and his need to be the curious, intelligent, active boy that he is. Lizbeth and her family showed us how

they came to supply three CSAs as well as numerous farmers markets. Through the Angel Family, we saw the importance of supporting small farmers as we work towards creating a sustainable food system for all; they've made it possible for hundreds of families in New York City to access locally grown food. Baby Ida is just starting out on her journey with food, health and life. Her mother Anna shared her thoughts about Ida's first foods and meal routines. Anna turns words into action and shows us never to assume we have all the answers. Lastly, Oliver jumped in feet first with his family's backyard fruit tree farm. He embodies the drive, optimism, dedication, smarts, and energy needed to connect the dots towards a more just food system.

The **What's On YOUR Plate?** community is a constantly evolving labor of love which sustains and nurtures those who engage with it. By reading this book, you're a part of it too. Let's celebrate what's on our plates.

Glossary

Agribusiness—A generic term for the various industries involved in food production, ranging from farming and food production, to manufacturing farm machinery and pesticides, to seed supply, to food wholesale and retail. The term has varying connotations, and in this book agribusiness refers to the small number of large, corporate entities that control much of these industries.

Biodegradable—Capable of being broken down, especially into innocuous products, by the action of living things (such as microorganisms).

Biodiversity—The number and variety of species in an ecosystem or biome. Biodiversity is one way of measuring the health of an ecosystem.

Bodega—A small store or shop that sells items such as candy, ice cream, soft drinks, lottery tickets, cigarettes, newspapers and magazines, along with a selection of processed food, and perhaps some groceries. These are similar to convenience stores, but are rarely owned by chains and are mostly seen in large cities, where they are very common.

Cellulosic Ethanol—A biofuel produced from wood, grasses, or the non-edible parts of plants. Biofuels are substances made from plants that can be used instead of gasoline or other fossil fuels.

Cold-Pressed (olive oil)—A process by which oil is extracted from olives without applying external heat. This process is generally considered a more environmentally sustainable way to gather olive oil.

Concentrated Animal Feeding Operation (CAFO)—An animal feeding facility that confines animals for more than 45 days at a time in an area that does not produce vegetation during the growing season, and the number of animals is equal to or over 1,000 cattle, 30,000 laying hens, etc. This is the official industry term for a "factory farm."

Conservation—The planned management of a natural resource to prevent exploitation, destruction, or neglect.

CSA (Community Supported Agriculture)—A socio-economic model of agriculture and food distribution. A CSA consists of a community of individuals who pledge support to a farming operation where the growers and consumers share the risks and benefits of food production. CSAs usually consist of a system of weekly delivery or pick-up of vegetables and fruit and sometimes includes dairy products and meat.

Diabetes—A variable disorder of carbohydrate metabolism caused by a combination of hereditary and environmental factors and usually characterized by inadequate secretion or utilization of insulin, by excessive urine production, by excessive amounts of sugar in the blood and urine, and by thirst, hunger, and loss of weight.

Fair Trade—A financial relationship between producers, sellers, and consumers based on the principle of equity within the exchange of goods. Generally, this means that consumers will pay a higher price for goods from sellers who guarantee a fair and transparent buying process, usually with a preference toward small or marginalized producers and environmentally sustainable practices.

Farm Bill—The primary agricultural and food policy tool of the United States government. The comprehensive omnibus bill is passed every 5 years or so by the United States Congress and deals with both agriculture and all other affairs under the purview of the United States Department of Agriculture.

Farmers Market—Markets usually held out-of-doors, in public spaces, where farmers can sell produce directly to the public.

Food Desert—A district with little or no

access to foods needed to maintain a healthy diet but often served by plenty of fast-food restaurants.

Free-range—A method of raising livestock in which the animals are allowed to range and forage with relative freedom, as opposed to being kept in cages or pens and fed there by farmers.

Grain-fed—Livestock (mainly cattle) that are given cereal grains or corn as feed. This decreases the time it takes to fatten the animals for slaughter and increases yield from dairy cattle.

Grass-fed—Livestock (mainly cattle) that are given grass as feed. This includes cattle that are let out to graze in pastures, but is not limited to free-range cattle. This has led to some controversy over whether the term is deceptive to consumers.

Greenwashing—The deceptive use of "green" PR or marketing in order to promote a misleading perception that a company's policies or products are environmentally friendly. The word is a combination of "green" and "whitewash."

Grower—Farmer.

Herbicides—Agents (usually chemical) used to destroy or inhibit plant growth.

High Cholesterol—The presence of high levels of cholesterol in the blood. It is not a disease but a metabolic derangement that can be secondary to many diseases and can contribute to many forms of disease, most notably cardiovascular disease.

High Fructose Corn Syrup (HFCS)—Any of a group of corn syrups that has undergone enzymatic processing to convert its glucose into fructose to produce a desired sweetness. In the United States, consumer foods and products typically use High Fructose Corn Syrup as a sugar substitute.

Insecticides—An agent (usually chemical) that destroys insects.

Junk Food—Food that may be appealing or enjoyable but is of little or no nutritional value.

Local—Nearby, within a particular area, or serving a specific area, as in a local business.

Locally grown—The definition of "locally grown" is not standardized: for buyers and vendors "local" can mean within an hour of where you live, a day's driving distance, or a source no more than 150–200 miles away.

Mad Cow Disease—AKA Bovine Spongiform Encephalopathy: a fatal, neurodegenerative disease in cattle that causes a spongy degeneration in the brain and spinal cord. It can be passed through infected food to humans.

Marine Certified—A label that appears on salmon that meets the standards of the Marine Stewardship Council (MSC). The Marine Certified label is seen by many as a marker of environmentally sustainable salmon fishing practices.

Monocropping—Raising only one crop on a farm. This is a very profitable method of farming, but it is less sustainable as it can lead to nutrient degradation in the soil.

"Off the Grid"—A social movement in which people move away from major centers of civilization. "The Grid" can refer to any sort of structure, from a city grid of streets to an electrical grid providing power.

Organic/Organic Farming—Farming methods, and food produced using these methods, in which no artificial or synthetic products, such as pesticides or antibiotics, are used.

Pastured Meat/Dairy—Meat or dairy derived from livestock that are fed by letting them out to graze. The term has a similar connotation to "free range."

Pesticides—Any agent used to kill or otherwise combat a predator or invasive species (such as insects or unwanted plants) that threaten a crop.

Plant-Centered Diet—A philosophy of eating endorsed by Anna Lappé and Michael

Pollan, among others, that allows for eating meat sparingly, but gives preference to plant products.

Producer—Farmer.

rBGH (recombinant bovine growth hormone)—A growth hormone that occurs naturally in cows but can be synthesized using recombinant DNA technology. Administering rBGH to dairy cows can dramatically increase their milk yield, but the use of rBGH has caused controversy due to possible health problems in both cows and humans.

Smart Choice Program—A rating system developed by a coalition of companies from the food industry. A "Smart Choice" label appears on products deemed to provide adequate nutrition and was devised to help consumers make nutritionally positive decisions when shopping for food. However, the system drew criticism for labeling Froot Loops, Lucky Charms, and Frosted Flakes as "Smart Choice," and was discontinued in October 2009.

(Government) Subsidy—A form of financial assistance paid to a business or economic sector by the government. Agricultural subsidies in the United States were originally established during the Great Depression to stabilize the prices of farm products by buying off produce when farmers harvested a surplus, and selling off that stored surplus during lean years, so that the amount on the market, and therefore prices, would remain stable. Since then, however, the questions of who gets subsidies and who controls them have become the subjects of controversy.

Supermarket—A large store that deals in staple foodstuffs, meats, produce, and dairy products, and usually household supplies.

Sustainability—the capacity to endure. The concept of sustainability relates to work practices in any industry or endeavor that uses limited resources. In farming, this means using methods that ensure the ability of the land to support continued farming far into the future, such as by avoiding nutrient loss and maintaining biodiversity. Sustainability takes on another meaning when buying and selling food, as it refers to sustainable food systems, which are able to keep large numbers of people employed and preserve the integrity of their communities over time.

Type 1 Diabetes—A form of diabetes usually diagnosed in children and young adults, previously known as juvenile diabetes. In type 1 diabetes, the body does not produce insulin, the hormone that is needed to convert sugar, starches and other food into energy.

Type 2 Diabetes—The most common form of diabetes. In type 2 diabetes, either the body does not produce enough insulin or the cells ignore the insulin.

Vegan—An adherent of veganism, a philosophy of eating in which people do not eat any foods that come from animals. This includes not only meat, but also foods like milk, eggs, and honey, which are produced by animals.

Vegetarian—An adherent of vegetarianism, a philosophy of eating in which people do not eat meat of any kind. Vegetarians may eat some animal products, such as milk, eggs, or honey, which are not strictly meat.

Vendor—In a supply chain, a vendor is anyone who provides goods or services to a company. In a food supply chain, vendors include stores like supermarkets or farmers' markets, as well as places that prepare food like restaurants.

Wild—Food that was not raised by a farmer under controlled conditions. Fish caught in the open ocean are wild, and so are fruits and vegetables that are picked from naturally occurring plants outside of farms.

Appendix: Questions and Answers

Below is an excerpt from Sadie and Safiyah's Q&A session with 1,400 schoolchildren who attended a screening of **What's On YOUR Plate?** at the Environmental Film Festival in the Nation's Capital.

Q: My question is: do you want to be a farmer?

SADIE & SAFIYAH: Yes.

Q: Have you all ever eaten snacks?

SAFIYAH: It's not like we are food angels. We still eat junk food every once in awhile. The point is not to never eat junk food. It's just to eat junk food as little as you can. If you have a bag of chips every once in awhile it's not going to kill you. If you have ice cream every once in awhile it's not going to kill you. It's just having enough healthy food to balance out the junk food.

Q: What was the most interesting place that you visited?

SADIE: The farm, definitely. Planting and harvesting with the Angel Family was really fun and really hard and really eye-opening. It looks like hard work. And it was hard work, but it was fun.

Q: What inspired you to make the movie?

SADIE: We want people to ask questions, and we want to inform people. We want them to eat healthy. We want people to be healthy.

SAFIYAH: We wanted to help people. We were really interested in this topic, so when you are interested in something you should just try to learn about it as much as you can, and then go out and share your knowledge with the world.

Q: Did you plan to change just New York's food habits, or the whole country?

SADIE: The whole country, definitely.

SAFIYAH: Internationally even. Just last year we went to Berlin and we talked to kids there.

Q: After making the movie did you find it harder to eat fast food, and non-organic?

SADIE: Definitely. After you actually know what you are eating, it's harder to eat it.

Q: Did this movie change your diet majorly? Or were you already eating healthily? And if there's a difference between the food you used to eat and the food you eat now, how does it change the way you feel?

SADIE: We were already eating pretty healthily. It changed my family's diet because we joined a CSA and we have more fresh food around the house. And I definitely feel better.

SAFIYAH: I can say that I wasn't eating as healthy before as I am now because I didn't know. And a lot of people don't know and that's because it's not a subject that gets talked about a lot in schools. So, that's why we made this movie. After we made the movie I was definitely more aware of what I was eating.

Q: Are you girls really vegetarian?

SADIE: Yes.

SAFIYAH: I've been a vegetarian my whole life. And a lot of people think that means that I don't eat cheese or yummy things, but I do.

SADIE: I was a vegetarian since I was nine.

Q: What is your favorite food?

SADIE: I like salads a lot, with a really good dressing. And with fruit in it, like strawberries.

SAFIYAH: I like almost everything.

Q: What's your favorite vegetable?

SADIE: My favorite vegetable is probably red peppers. I really like those because they're easy and you can just munch on them anytime.

Q: How does it feel at the end of the day when you know you have helped someone?

SADIE: It feels amazing.

SAFIYAH: It's really good to see the progress—that kids are really making changes and schools are really making changes because the changes are for the better. We hope that we can continue to help people.

SADIE: You guys can make it happen, you just have to speak up—you have voices too. A lot of people think just because you are kids, that adults rule the world—but you guys have just as much of a voice. So you can write your Congressman or something, and just keep speaking up.

Selected Resources

BOOKS AND BLOGS

The Curious Garden, by Peter Brown. A wonderfully written and drawn picture-book about a tiny garden in the city that grows into something amazing.

Diet for a Hot Planet, by Anna Lappé. The whole story of how our food system affects the entire planet, and how we can change the world by changing what we eat.

Fed Up with School Lunch, (http://fedupwithschoollunch.blogspot.com). Mrs. Q's blog is a window into world of school lunch, a world that many grown-ups have forgotten about, and has probably changed a bit since those grown-ups were kids.

Food Politics, (www.foodpolitics.com). Is NYU professor/food activist Marion Nestle's blog about food reform and food politics issues.

Go Green East Harlem, by Scott Stringer (editor). The bilingual four-color Go Green East Harlem Cookbook, which features healthy recipes by East Harlem residents.

Grub: Ideas for an Urban Organic Kitchen, by Anna Lappé and Bryant Terry. A great, healthy organic cookbook for city dwellers, which pairs recipes and art.

Kids in the Garden, by Elizabeth McCorquodale. A fun, friendly, colorful guide to involving kids in gardening with activities an recipes for kids and tips for composting and seed saving.

La Vida Locavore, (http://www.lavidalocavore.org/). Is a wonderful blog/forum/general resource for people who want to eat local food in the USA, with writers from all over the country.

A Little Piece of Earth: How to Grow Your Own Food in Small Spaces, by Maria Finn. Being an "urban farmer" doesn't mean you have to have a huge garden on your roof, you can grow food even in the smallest apartment. Includes lovely drawings and recipes.

The Omnivore's Dilemma: Young Readers Edition, by Michael Pollan. A version of the bestselling look at where our food comes from made for middle school students.

Salad People and More Real Recipes, by Mollie Katzen. A great cookbook with recipes that young kids (preschoolers and up) can enjoy making and eating.

Vegan Soul Kitchen, by Bryant Terry. 150 recipes for delicious, healthy, vegan food, each with a soundtrack recommendation for music to cook by. Dancing in the kitchen can make your food taste better.

Worms Eat Our Garbage, by Mary Appelhof, Mary Frances Fenton, and Barbara Loss Harris. A curriculum of classroom activities based around the earthworm. Includes information about waste management, environmentalism, and ecology. Grades 4-8.

ORGANIZATIONS

Children's Aid Society, (http://www.childrensaidsociety.org/). A top-rated, New York-based children's charity providing critical services to children and their families.

East New York Farms! (http://www.eastnewyorkfarms.org/). Organizes youth and adults to address food justice in our community by promoting local sustainable agriculture and community-led economic development

Eat Well, (http://www.eatwellguide.org/). A free, online database for finding fresh, locally grown, and sustainably produced food in the United States and Canada.

Edible Schoolyard, (http://www.edibleschoolyard.org/). A one-acre organic garden and kitchen classroom for urban public school students at Martin Luther King, Jr. Middle School in Berkeley, California. Student participation in all aspects of growing, harvesting, and preparing nutritious, seasonal produce.

Environmental Working Group, (http://www.ewg.org/). Research that brings to light unsettling facts that you have a right to know. It shames and shakes up polluters and their lobbyists. It rattles politicians and shapes policy. It persuades bureaucracies to rethink science and strengthen regulation. It provides practical information you can use to protect your family and community.

Food Routes, (http://foodroutes.org/). A national, nonprofit organization that provides communications tools, technical support, networking, and information resources to organizations nationwide that are working to rebuild local, community-based food systems.

Growing Power, (http://www.growingpower.org/). A national nonprofit organization and land trust supporting people from diverse backgrounds, and the environments in which they live, by helping to provide equal access to healthy, high-quality, safe and affordable food for people in all communities.

GrowNYC, (http://www.grownyc.org/). A hands-on non-profit which improves New York City's quality of life through environmental programs transforming communities block by block and empowering all New Yorkers to secure a clean and healthy environment for future generations.

Harvest Home Farmers Markets, (http://www. harvesthomefm.org/). Committed to making farm fresh produce available to neighborhoods with limited access, and to strengthening local communities by providing a place where residents can come together to share ideas, improve nutrition and support local agriculture.

Just Food, (http://www.justfood.org/). A non-profit organization operating in the greater New York City region to address the economic justice, environmental sustainability and food sovereignty needs of regional family farmers, community gardeners and underserved NYC neighborhoods.

Local Harvest, (http://www.localharvest.org). Maintains a definitive and reliable, "living" public, nationwide directory of small farms, farmers markets, and other local food sources.

Let's Move! (http://www.letsmove.gov/). A campaign, started by First Lady Michelle Obama, has an ambitious national goal of solving the challenge of childhood obesity within a generation.

Lunch Lessons, (http://www.chefann.com/). Chef Ann Cooper is working to transform cafeterias into culinary classrooms for students — one school lunch at a time.

National Farm to School Network, (http://www. farmtoschool.org/). Sprouted from the desire to support community-based food systems, strengthen family farms, and improve student health by reducing childhood obesity.

New Farmer Development Project, (http:// www.grownyc.org/greenmarket/nfdp). Identifies, educates, and supports immigrants with agricultural experience by helping them become local farmers and establish small farms in the New York City region.

Slow Food USA, (http://www.slowfoodusa.org/). A non-profit, eco-gastronomic, member-supported organization founded in 1989 to counteract fast food and fast life, the disappearance of local food traditions, and people's dwindling interest in the food they eat, where it comes from, how it tastes, and how our food choices affect the rest of the world.

South Bronx Food Cooperative, (http://www.sbxfc. org/). A shopping alternative to the profit-oriented commercial food markets found in the Bronx.

Spoons Across America, (http://spoonsacrossamerica. org/). A not-for-profit organization that works to influence the eating habits of children through hands-on education that celebrates their connection to local farmers and the important tradition of sharing meals around the family table.

Stone Barns Center for Food and Agriculture, (http://www.stonebarnscenter.org/). Is a farm and a restaurant whose goal is to celebrate, teach and advance community-based food production and enjoyment, from farm to classroom to table.

Sustainable Table, (http://www.sustainabletable. org). Created to help consumers understand the problems with our food supply and offer viable solutions and alternatives.

The Urban Farmers, (http://www.theurbanfarmers.org). A non-profit organization based in the San Francisco Bay area, dedicated to changing our food system to better address the needs of people and the planet we inhabit.

Notes

Listed below, by chapter, are the sources for information referred to in the text. Website links are current as of October 2010.

INTRO

Ayala, Guadalupe X. et al. "Away-From-Home Food Intake and Risk for Obesity: Examining the Influence of Context." *Obesity, A Research Journal* (2008). (http://www.nature.com/oby/journal/v16/n5/full/oby200834a.html)

Escarce José J. "Family Structure and Childhood Obesity, Early Childhood Longitudinal Study—Kindergarten Cohort." Centers for Disease Control and Prevention. 2010. (http://www.cdc.gov/PCD/issues/2010/may/09_0156.htm) In a study by the Centers for Disease Control and Prevention, researchers found that 13% of kindergarteners, nearly 21% of third graders, and 24% of fifth graders were obese.

Schlosser, Eric. *Fast Food Nation*. New York: Harper Perennial, 2005.

CHAPTER 1

The Corn Refiners Association. SweetSurprise.com. The Corn Refiners Association. 2009. (http://www.sweetsurprise.com)

Fishel, Frederick M. "Pesticide Use Trends in the U.S.: Global Comparison." University of Florida, Institute of Food and Agricultural Services Extension (2007). (https://edis.ifas.ufl.edu/pi180)

Funch, Flemming H. "Analysis of Residues in Seven Pesticides in Some Fruits and Vegetables by Means of High Pressure Liquid Chromatography." *European Food Research and Technology*, Vol. 173, No. 2 (1981). (http://www.springerlink.com/content/r107363272586767/)

Hunter, Alna. "Fructose May Increase Blood Pressure." *CBS News Health Blog*. CBS News. 2010. (http://www.cbsnews.com/8301-504763_162-20009722-10391704.html)

Madison Area Community Supported Agriculture Coalition. "CSA Healthy Rebates." Madison Area Community Supported Agriculture Coalition. (http://www.macsac.org/rebates.html)

Nestle, Marion. "Kids Deserve Better." *The Daily Green*. 2008.

Sustainable Table. "The Issues: rBGH." *Sustainable Table*. July 2009. (http://www.sustainabletable.org/issues/rbgh/)

CHAPTER 2

American Diabetes Association. "Living with Diabetes: African Americans & Complications." American Diabetes Association. (http://www.diabetes.org/living-with-diabetes/complications/african-americans-and-complications.html)

Popkin, Barry M. "Global Nutrition Dynamics: The World Is Shifting Rapidly Toward Diet Linked with Noncommunicable Diseases." *The American Journal of Clinical Nutrition*, Vol. 84 (2006): pp. 289–298.

CHAPTER 3

Adamick, Kate. "'Food Revolution': A School Lunch Expert Reacts." *The Atlantic*. 2010. (http://www.theatlantic.com/food/archive/2010/04/food-revolution-a-school-lunch-expert-reacts/38479/)

ECO Lunchbox. "Lunchbox Waste Study 2010 Results." *ECO Lunchbox*. 2009. (http://www.ecolunchboxes.com/why_facts.html)

Eisnitz, Gail A. *Slaughterhouse: The Shocking Story of Greed, Neglect, and Inhumane Treatment Inside the U.S. Meat Industry*. New York: Prometheus Books, 2007.

Mission: Readiness. "Too Fat to Fight." *Military Leaders for Kids*. Mission: Readiness, 2010.

Mrs. Q. "The School Lunch Project." *Markbittman.com*. Mark Bittman. 2010. (http://markbittman.com/the-school-lunch-project)

———. "Fed Up with School Lunch." (http://fedupwithschoollunch.blogspot.com) See the lunches Mrs. Q ate. (http://www.fns.usda.gov/cnd/lunch/aboutlunch/NSLPFactSheet.pdf)

New York State Council on Food Policy. "Summer Meeting 2010, Panel: NYS Food System 'Supply, Demand and Delivery' Minutes." New York State Council on Food Policy. 28 June 2010. (http://www.nyscfp.org/docs/activities/NYSCFP_Panel Mins_6_28_10.pdf)

NYC Department of "Childhood Obesity is a Serious Concern in New York City" in *NYC Vital Signs*, 2009. (http://www.nyc.gov/html/doh/downloads/pdf/survey/survey2009fitnessgram.pdf)

U.S. Department of Agriculture. "National School Lunch Program Fact Sheet." U.S. Department of Agriculture. September 2010. (http://www.fns.usda.gov/cnd/lunch/aboutlunch/NSLPFactSheet.pdf)

CHAPTER 4

Woolston, Chris. "Type 2 Diabetes: Growing Epidemic Among Teens." CVS/pharmacy. 2009. (http://www.cvshealthresources.com/topic/type2kids)

CHAPTER 5

Circle of Responsibility. "Beef Raised Without the Routine Use of Antibiotics." Accessed 2010. (http://www.circleofresponsibility.com/page/301/reduced-antibiotics.htm)

Environmental Working Group. "United States Farm Subsidy Program Summary." Environmental Working Group. (http://farm.ewg.org/region?fips=00000&regname=UnitedStatesFarmSubsidySummary)

Forschunginstitut für biologischen Landbau, International Federation of Organic Agriculture Movements. "Table:World: Organic Agriculture by Country: Organic Agricultural Land, Share of Total Agricultural Land, Producers 2008." 2010. (http://www.organic-world.net/statistics-world-area-producers.html)

Ganzel, Bill. "Farming in the 1950s and 60s." Wessels Living History Farm. 2007. (http://www.livinghistoryfarm.org/farminginthe50s/farminginthe1950s.html)

Mazoyer, Marcel, Roudart, Laurence. *A History of World Agriculture: From the Neolithic to the Current Crisis*. London: Earthscan, 2006.

Miller, G. Tyler & Scott Spoolman, *Living in the Environment*. Brooks/Cole: CA, 2009. p. 304.

Pollan, Michael. "You Are What You Grow." *Michael pollan.com. New York Times Magazine*. 2007. (http://michaelpollan.com/articles-archive/you-are-what-you grow)

U.S. Bureau of Labor Statistics. "Section 11, Agriculture, Forestry, Fishing and Hunting." *Occupational Employment Statistics: May 2009 National Industry Specific Occupational Employment and Wage Estimates*. U.S. Bureau of Labor Statistics, 2010. (http://www.bls.gov/oes/current/naics2_11.htm#top)

CHAPTER 6

Committee on Pesticides in the Diets of Infants and Children, National Research Council. *Pesticides in the Diets of Infants and Children*. Washington, D.C. : National Academy Press, 1993.

Lappé, Anna. *Diet for a Hot Planet*. New York: Bloomsbury, 2010. p. 21

Nestle, Marion. "Raise Your Hand for Chocolate Milk?" *Lunch Lessons. Chefann.com.* 2009. (http://www.chefann.com/blog/archives/1624)

U.S. Department of Agriculture. "FY 2011 Budget Appendix. p. 80." U.S. Department of Agriculture. (http://www.usda.gov/wps/portal/usda/usdahome?navid=BUDGET)

———. "State Fact Sheets, Organic Agriculture and Farm Characteristics." 2007. (http://www.ers.usda.gov/statefacts/us.htm)

CHAPTER 7

Bennett, Lisa. "Responding to the School Garden Debate," *The Center for Ecoliteracy Blog*. The Center for Ecoliteracy. 2010. (http://www.ecoliteracy.org/blog/responding-school-garden-debate)

Clean Air Council. "Waste Facts and Figures." Clean Air Council. (http://www.cleanair.org/Waste/wasteFacts.html)

Edible Schoolyard. "Missions and Goals." Edible Schoolyard. (http://www.edibleschoolyard.org/mission-goals)

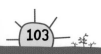

Index

Bold page numbers indicate more substantive treatment of the topic.

Acknowledgements

The **What's On YOUR Plate?** project is part of a vibrant, hopeful, and global effort to improve people's lives and the life of the planet. I thank all those involved for their leadership, their passion and their vision.

In particular, writing this book has been a delicious and dynamic collaboration. Mary Jeys exudes thoroughness, calm, intelligence, and creativity, all of which she brought to her work on this book. She kept us on track and online. Check. Plus. She also collaborated on graphic design and layout with Cassie Wagler, who's not only clever, careful and committed but also a second-generation composter. The activities shine because of Cassie's attention. India Amos patiently joined us in the final, long stretches of layout and design and was a tremendous help in pulling it all together.

The insightful and whimsical Nate Buckley regularly pitched in with research, layout and turns of phrase. Further, I thank Nate and the smart and reliable Angelica Modabber, for being the voice of **WOYP?** on the Internet. For spending days in the office, bringing fresh insights to the drafts, and gamely taking on whatever came their way, thanks go to Elona Jones, Arlo Paust, Bria Lewis, and Geraldo Arias.

I thank all of our readers for sharing their time and their smarts: Winsome Brown, Tracy Candido, Farai Chideya, Ellen Fried, Anna Lappé, Karina Mangu-Ward, and Amy Richards. Also, thanks to the Travelling Gourmet Rita Tyler for making sure our recipes work. For being generous with their advice, I thank Harriet Bell, Joy De Menil, Alane Mason, Eric Rayman, and Jennifer Rubell. For designing our website, thanks to futurefarmers. And thanks to Chris Kennedy and Fronsy Thurman for collaborating on our curriculum.

My dear friend and the **WOYP?** film's brilliant producer, Tanya Selvaratnam, appeared just in time to help edit the scattered drafts into a coherent and textured expression of community. For reading several drafts of every chapter, and for swimming past the boundaries with me, I'm thankful to Julie Tolentino. My deep gratitude goes to Jared Koch for connecting the dots and demonstrating exemplary trust.

Big shout out to my brain-food suppliers: David Abbott, Jamie Bennett, Majora Carter, Ken Cook, David DeGennaro, Gita Drury, Deb Eschmeyer, Maria Finn, DeeDee Halleck, Anna Hammond, Van Jones, Mia Juhng, Jonathan Kevles, Kristen Mancinelli, Kelly Moltzen, Scot Nakagawa, Julie Negrin, Kimberly Perry (and super shout out for writing the Foreword!), Michael Pollan, Dr. Rob Saken, Bryant Terry, Latham Thomas, and many others who kept me busy discussing both fact and opinion and who shared daily news items, blogs, links, and good ideas related to school food, local food and food related health-issues.

For always bringing their strengths and their love, for being at the core of my family, and for making my life an unambiguous pleasure, special thanks go to Telma Abascal, Paul Armstrong, Sabina Balvin, Leslie Belzberg, Lisa Boone, Kate Clinton, Lissette Delgado, Susan Dupré, Muna El Fituri, Laurie Engle, Uchenna Enwezor, Giselle Fernandez, Stosh Fila, Lola Flash, Marta and Julien Florez, Agnes Gund, Susannah Gund, Bryan Haynes, Sarah Ingersoll, Ngina Johnson, Shalini Kantayya, Vivien Labaton, Giuseppe Lignano, George McCann, Marques McClary, Heather Moore, Pascale and Lily Ouattara, Jess, Kaya and Zoe Saalfield, Greg Sax, Daniel Shapiro, Stephan Shaw, the Traggio Family (especially Ellie for the farm and kitchen on our cover!), Urvashi Vaid, Sunita Vishwanath, Ouattara Watts, and Dana Yeminy.

The children and parents included in this book are wonderful, open, and creative travelers, and I appreciate that they so willingly and honestly let us in on their adventures. I'm particularly grateful to Ana, Anna, Cathy, John, Marcia, and Rachel.

My three sons, Kofi, Rio and Tenzin, shine their gorgeous light in all corners. They keep me focused on what's true, miraculous and fun in the everyday process of growing up.

Finally, of course, this project wouldn't exist without my amazing daughter Sadie and her fabulous friend Safiyah. I'm so lucky to have spent these years learning with them. Each day, they reminded me how honest and productive curiosity can be. Special thanks to them for the inspiration, and for seeing this project through.